SHOP GUIDE

PIPE FITTINGS

NIPPLES   PIPE LENGTHS UP TO 22 FT.   STRAIGHT COUPLING   REDUCING COUPLING

STRAIGHT TEE   REDUCING TEE   STREET TEE   STRAIGHT CROSS   REDUCING CROSS

90° ELBOW   45° ELBOW   REDUCING ELBOW   90° STREET ELBOW   45° STREET ELBOW   45° Y-BEND

UNION (3 PARTS)   PLUG   BUSHING   CAP   RETURN BEND

90°   45°   STREET   UNION TEES

UNION ELBOWS

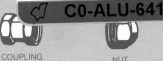

COUPLING   NUT   CAP

90° ELBOW   90° ELBOW

REDUCING TEE   REDUCER

PLUG   45° ELBOW   TEE

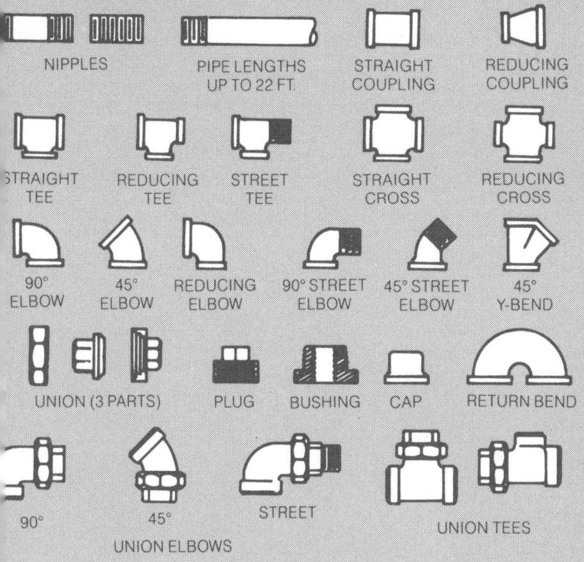

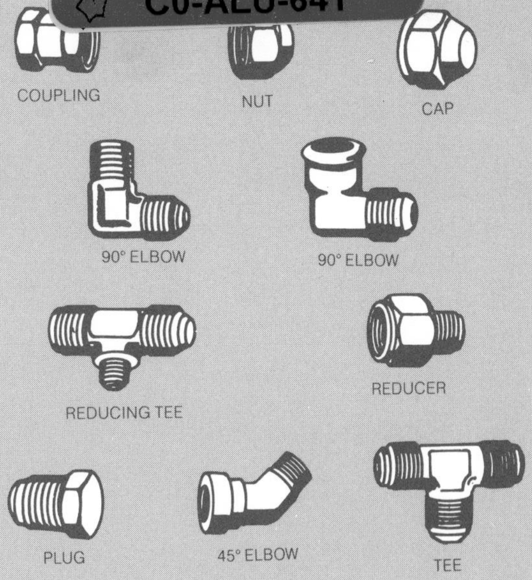

MEASURES OF CAPACITY

1 cup	=	8 fl oz
2 cups	=	1 pint
2 pints	=	1 quart
4 quarts	=	1 gallon
2 gallons	=	1 peck
4 pecks	=	1 bushel

STANDARD STEEL PIPE ((All Dimensions in inches)

Nominal Size	Outside Diameter	Inside Diameter	Nominal Size	Outside Diameter	Inside Diameter
1/8	0.405	0.269	1	1.315	1.049
1/4	0.540	0.364	1¼	1.660	1.380
3/8	0.675	0.493	1½	1.900	1.610
1/2	0.840	0.622	2	2.375	2.067
3/4	1.050	0.824	2½	2.875	2.469

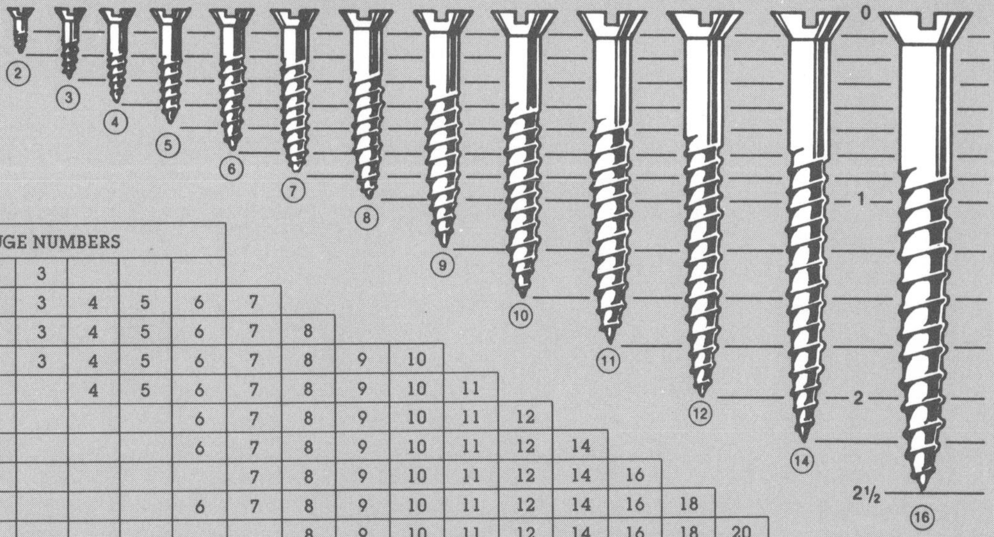

WOOD SCREWS

LENGTH	GAUGE NUMBERS													
	0	1	2	3										
¼ INCH	0	1	2	3										
3/8 INCH			2	3	4	5	6	7						
½ INCH			2	3	4	5	6	7	8					
5/8 INCH				3	4	5	6	7	8	9	10			
¾ INCH					4	5	6	7	8	9	10	11		
7/8 INCH							6	7	8	9	10	11	12	
1 INCH							6	7	8	9	10	11	12	14
1¼ INCH								7	8	9	10	11	12	14	16
1½ INCH						6	7	8	9	10	11	12	14	16	18
1¾ INCH								8	9	10	11	12	14	16	18	20
2 INCH								8	9	10	11	12	14	16	18	20
2¼ INCH									9	10	11	12	14	16	18	20
2½ INCH											12	14	16	18	20
2¾ INCH											14	16	18	20
3 INCH												16	18	20
3½ INCH													18	20	24
4 INCH													18	20	24

WHEN YOU BUY SCREWS, SPECIFY (1) LENGTH, (2) GAUGE NUMBER, (3) TYPE OF HEAD—FLAT, ROUND, OR OVAL, (4) MATERIAL—STEEL, BRASS, BRONZE, ETC., (5) FINISH—BRIGHT, STEEL BLUED, CADMIUM, NICKEL, OR CHROMIUM PLATED.

Popular Mechanics

do-it-yourself encyclopedia

The complete, illustrated home reference guide from the world's most authoritative source for today's how-to-do-it information.

Volume 6

CIRCULAR SAWS

to

DARKROOM TECHNIQUES

HEARST DIRECT BOOKS

NEW YORK

Acknowledgements

The Popular Mechanics Encyclopedia is published with the consent and cooperation of POPULAR MECHANICS Magazine.

For POPULAR MECHANICS Magazine:

Editor-in-Chief: *Joe Oldham*
Managing Editor: *Bill Hartford*
Special Features Editor: *Sheldon M. Gallager*
Automotive Editor: *Wade A. Hoyt, SAE*
Home and Shop Editor: *Steve Willson*
Electronics Editor: *Stephen A. Booth*
Boating, Outdoors and Travel Editor: *Timothy H. Cole*
Science Editor: *Dennis Eskow*

Popular Mechanics Encyclopedia

Project Director: *Boyd Griffin*
Manufacturing: *Ron Schoenfeld*
Assistant Editors: *Cynthia W. Lockhart, Peter McCann, Rosanna Petruccio*
Production Coordinator: *Peter McCann*

The staff of Popular Mechanics Encyclopedia is grateful to the following individuals and organizations:

Editor: *C. Edward Cavert*
Editor Emeritus: *Clifford B. Hicks*
Production: *Layla Productions*
Production Director: *Lori Stein*
Book Design: *The Bentwood Studio*
Art Director: *Jos. Trautwein*
Design Consultant: *Suzanne Bennett & Associates*
Illustrations: *AP Graphics, Evelyne Johnson Associates, Popular Mechanics Magazine, Vantage Art.*

Contributing Writers: Ivan Berger, *Cure muddy photo prints*, page 758; *Load your own 35-mm film cartridges*, page 762; John Burroughs, *Clamp selection and use*, page 658; Walter E. Burton, *Machine-vise clamp*, page 663; Rosario Capotosto, *Countertop installation in tile or laminate*, page 744; Christopher Crandall, *Darkroom goofs you can avoid*, page 754; Richard Day, *Concrete block laying tips*, page 727; E. A. Franks, *Deburring jig makes saw cut smoother*, page 652; Frank L. Greenwald, *Connecticut shelf clock*, page 665; George L. Hall, *Computers: an introduction*, page 679; *Flat-screen displays*, page 695; *Communicating with computers*, page 700; *Computer care and repair*, page 711; Bill Hartford, *Coolant recovery system installation*, page 738; R.S. Hedin, *Bar clamps you can make*, page 662; Len Hilts, *Cast your own patio slabs*, page 721; Wayne C. Leckey, *Closets you can build in*, page 673; Emery J. Loiselle, *Portable saw bench you can build*, page 654; Walter Salm, *Computer monitors*, page 689; Mort Schultz, *Cooling system maintenance*, page 733; *Protect your car against the cold*, page 740; Harry Wicks, *Circular saw know-how*, page 644.

Picture Credits: Popular Mechanics Encyclopedia is grateful to the following for permission to reprint their photographs: Apple Computer, Inc., pages 681 (top) and 682; AT & T Bell Laboratories, page 681 (bottom); Commodore Systems Division, page 684; Data General, pages 696 (top) and 697; Hayes Microcomputer Products, Inc., page 704 (top left); Courtesy of International Business Machines (IBM), pages 679 (bottom), and 704 (bottom left); Cynthia Lockhart, pages 687 (top), 711, 712 (left and right); Misco Inc., Computer Supplies, pages 705 and 716 (bottom); Photo Resolutions, page 679 (top); Portland Cement Association, page 721; Prometheus Products, Inc., page 704 (center left); Siecor Corp., page 707; Sperry/Univac, page 680; Xerox Corp., page 689.

ISBN 0-87851-159-8

Library of Congress 85-81760

10 9 8 7 6 5 4

PRINTED IN THE UNITED STATES OF AMERICA

Contents

VOLUME 6 • CI to DA

CIRCULAR SAWS
Circular saw know-how 644
Saw blade selection 648
Carbide blades—performance at a price . 650
Deburring jig makes saw cut smoother 652
Portable saw bench you can build 654
See also Power Tools . . . . Vol. 19
See also Radial-Arm Saws . . . . Vol. 20

CITIZEN BAND RADIO
See Electronics . . . . Vol. 8

CLAMPS
Clamp selection and use 658
Bar clamps you can make 662
Machine-vise clamp 663

CLOCKS
Connecticut shelf clock 665
Heirlom wall clock 669
Wall clock from your lathe 671

CLOSETS
Closets you can build in 673
Make your closets work 676

CODES: BUILDING
See Homes . . . . Vol. 13

CODES: ELECTRICAL
See Electrical Wiring . . . . Vol. 8

COFFEE TABLES
See Tables . . . . Vol. 23

COLONIAL FURNITURE
See Furniture Projects . . . . Vol. 9

COMBINATION SQUARE
See Hand Tools . . . . Vol. 12

COMPUTERS
Computers: an introduction 679
Computer monitors 690
Flat screen displays 696
Communicating with computers 702
Computer system hookups 708
Computer care and repair 711
Computer workstation 716
    See Weather Instruments . . . . Vol. 25

CONCRETE
Cast your own patio slabs 721
Concrete slabs—pour them yourself 723

CONCRETE BLOCKS
Concrete block laying tips 727
See also Stairs . . . . Vol. 22

CONSTRUCTION
See Carpentry . . . . Vol. 5

COOLING SYSTEMS: AUTO
Cooling system maintenance 733
Engine overheating troubleshooting 737
Coolant recovery system installation 738

COLD WEATHER PROTECTION: AUTO
Protect your car against the cold 740

COUNTERTOPS
Countertop installation in tile or laminate . 744
Plastic laminate application 751
See also Kitchens . . . . Vol. 14.
See also Tile . . . . Vol. 24

CRAFTS
See Hobbies . . . . Vol. 12

CUPBOARDS
See Cabinets . . . . Vol. 4

CUTOFF MACHINES
See Power Tools . . . . Vol. 19

CUTTERS
See Metalworking . . . . Vol. 16

DADO
See Joinery . . . . Vol. 14

DARKROOM TECHNIQUES
Darkroom goofs you can avoid 755
Cure muddy photo prints 759
Load your own 35-mm film cartridges 763
Darkroom tips for photographers 765
See also Darkroom Projects . . . . Vol. 7
See also Photography . . . . Vol. 18

INDEX 767

Don't electrocute your car battery 253
See also Charging System, Auto . . . . Vol. 5

BEAMS
See Ceilings . . . . Vol. 5
INDEX 255

Circular saw know-how

■ IT DOESN'T TAKE very long for anyone interested in do-it-yourself jobs to realize that a portable circular saw is a "must-have" tool. With a power saw, you will be able to do your cutting a lot faster with considerably less effort than ever before. What is often surprising to a first-time saw owner is just how much a circular saw—used properly—will upgrade craftsmanship.

Be aware there is a certain hazard involved when cutting with a portable saw. As with most tools—hand and power—common sense plays a very important role when it comes to safety. Once you understand the tool and how to handle it correctly, you will wonder how you ever got along without it.

As you view a circular saw from its right side, the spinning blade rotates in a counterclockwise direction. This means that the blade does its cutting on the "upstroke." For this reason, whenever it makes a difference the cutting is always done with the "good," or "decorative," side down.

Circular saws are generally described by size: for example, 7-incher, 7¼-in. and the like. This size denotes the maximum-diameter blade that the saw will accommodate. A 7¼-in. saw is generally considered most desirable by do-it-

TYPICAL CIRCULAR saw includes a rip guide and blade wrench.

yourselfers. Larger-diameter, more expensive saws are available, but these are intended primarily for builders.

With a 7¼-in. saw you can cut through 2-in. stock effortlessly—even when the saw is set to cut at a 45° bevel. When you must cut heavier stock such as a 4x4, you can do it with two passes.

Most circular-saw motors are of the universal type that operate at voltages within 5 percent above or below that indicated on the tool's specification plate. Also check the plate for the

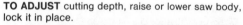

TO ADJUST cutting depth, raise or lower saw body, lock it in place.

OTHER METHOD is to change depth by pivoting, as this saw does.

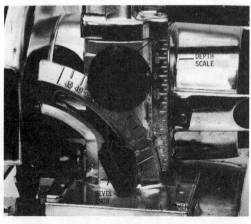

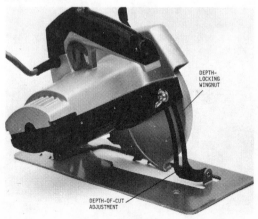

type of power circuit on which it is designed to operate. Many saws can be used on both a.c. and a.c.-d.c.

To protect yourself from electric shock, work only with a tool that is either grounded or double-insulated. If not of the double-insulated variety, your saw should come with a three-prong grounding plug. If you must use an extension cord, use only a three-conductor type so a continuous grounding circuit is provided. Also, make certain that the conductor size of the cord is large enough to prevent an excessive voltage drop.

All circular saws have retractable blade guards. As the saw is pushed into the work the guard retracts into the saw's upper blade housing—leaving the portion of the blade below the workpiece exposed. Develop the habit of making certain that the blade guard is operational before starting the saw—*every time*. You want to be certain that the guard snaps back to its lower position before setting down with a spinning blade. *Never, under any circumstances, remove the blade guard from your saw.*

Always keep the saw away from your body when the blade is spinning, and *never* walk away from the tool while the blade is still in motion. And don't forget this (very) basic rule—always disconnect power before changing blades.

Finally, read the manufacturer's manual before using the tool.

In broadest terms, three factors will affect your decision when picking a saw: materials, comfort and cost.

Materials. Obviously, you need a saw with extra power if you intend to use it primarily to

HOLDING BLADE against wood prevents movement as arbor nut is tightened.

GOOD JOB TABLE: Two sawhorses and three 2x3s. Cutoff is over a single 2x3.

TO DETERMINE blade depth, place saw on stock; use minimal projection.

FOR SAFETY, saw weight should be on workpiece, not cutoff.

Basic cutting techniques

CORRECT SAW-HOLDING technique is to clamp work and use both hands.

IMPROMPTU RIP GUIDE—thumb and finger squeeze saw shoe, travel with board edge.

TO RIP narrow piece accurately, lock the rip guide, make it ride work edge.

SOME MITER guides are adjustable for angle-cutting. When possible, clamp guide.

COMPOUND-ANGLE cut is made by setting saw at desired bevel, using miter guide.

TO CUT plywood sheets, you can use a 4-ft. T-square clamped to the work-piece.

Plywood blades

Sears' ply-tooth

Skil's plywood

Rockwell's plywood

Other cuts you can make

TO JOIN boards at angle, tack boards together and cut them simultaneously.

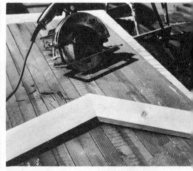

CUT THIS way, boards fit perfectly, even if you stray from cutting line.

TWO GROOVING techniques (above and right): Make overlapping passes

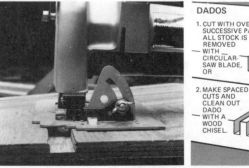

DADOS

1. CUT WITH OVERLAPPING SUCCESSIVE PASSES- ALL STOCK IS REMOVED WITH CIRCULAR- SAW BLADE, OR

2. MAKE SPACED CUTS AND CLEAN OUT DADO WITH A WOOD CHISEL.

OR ROUGH CUT dado with spaced kerfs, finish groove by cleaning with a chisel.

N YOU crosscut rough work, a oned thumb can be a guide.

IF NEATNESS is important, always use a miter guide.

URE of accuracy on long cuts a tacked-on guide.

USE A SLOW feed for bevel cutting because the saw tends to drift.

cut concrete or steel. But there's no need to pay for all that power if your work will be confined mostly to wood.

Comfort. The tool has to feel good to *you*— you're the one who will use it. Never buy a tool without some type of personal-use test—even if it is strictly a simulation-use in the store.

Cost. Make no mistake about the fact that you get what you pay for. A $20 saw, for example, will indeed cut 2x4s, but don't expect it to do this all day and survive. A $75 tool will.

Once you own a saw, get to know it. Be aware that the saw must always be firmly held, and that a two-hand grip is best. If you must use one hand to hold the work, keep that hand well away from the cutting line.

Also, keep your body to the side of the cutting line. Set the blade to project about ⅛-in. or so below the work. For a good worktable setup, use two sawhorses, and three lengths of two-by stock.

Rate of feed is important: Never push the saw so there is a strain on its motor. The density of material being cut and the type of blade used dictate the feed rate.

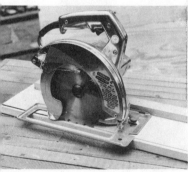

TO CUT edge rabbet, make the first pass with a guide temporarily nailed to work.

THEN CLAMP work in vise and tack guide to workbench top for the second pass.

HEFTY WORKPIECE can be cut by making passes from opposite sides of the board.

SAW MUST ride cutoff position, clamp ork, hold tool with two hands.

PLUNGE CUT is made by slowly lowering the spinning blade into workpiece.

BEFORE CUTTING fourth line, tack support strip to keep blade from binding.

Saw blade selection

■ WHEN ONE TYPE of saw blade is used to cut all kinds of material, it's almost like using one size nail to build a house. Only when a plywood blade is used to cut plywood, or a hardboard blade is used to cut hardboard, for example, can you turn out the best work and get the most from your bench saw or portable power saw.

That's why a selection of blades having a wide range of tooth patterns is available, each designed to cut a specific material in the best, fastest and smoothest way.

For general-purpose cutting, both with and across grain, a flat combination blade is your best bet, but, again, it won't match the extra-smooth cut you get with a hollow-ground planer blade. Thus it's important to keep several types of saw blades on hand so you can switch from one to the other, whatever your cutting requirements.

Carbide-tip blade

Combination blade (hollow ground)

Plywood blade

Rip blade

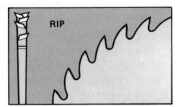

FOR RIPPING all hardwoods and softwoods. Has heavy hub and is taper-ground for extra clearance.

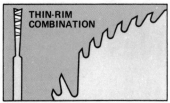

FINEST combination blade for fine trim and finish work. Use it to rip, crosscut or miter.

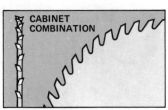

CABINETMAKER'S combination blade cuts in any direction through either hardwoods or softwoods.

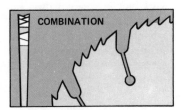

CABINETMAKER'S blade. Produces smooth and accurate cuts in any direction in hardwoods.

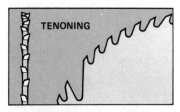

ALL-PURPOSE blade is wide-kerfed for cutting tenons and splines in all hardwoods and softwoods.

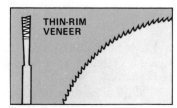

FOR SATIN-SMOOTH finish cuts in either plywood or thin veneers without splintering.

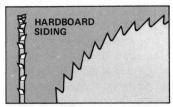

BEST BLADE for cutting tempered hardboard underlayment, siding and perforated board.

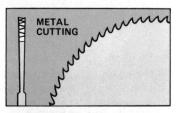

INTENDED for aluminum, brass, bronze, copper, zinc and lead. A truly professional blade.

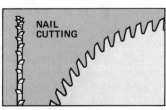

FOR ROUGH-CUTTING (rip and crosscut) through all woods that have an occasional nail.

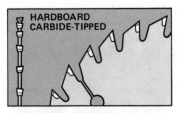

EXCELLENT FOR WOOD, but can also be used on hardboard siding. Its 32 teeth cut fast and straight.

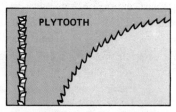

FINE-TOOTH, smooth-cutting blade for plywood, composition board, softboard and the like.

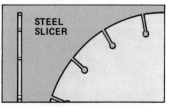

FOR LIGHT-GAUGE sheet steel, roofing, guttering and downspouts, up to 1/16-in. thick.

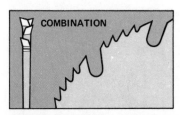

GOOD FOR RIPPING, crosscutting and mitering on all hardwoods and softwoods. Comes taper-ground.

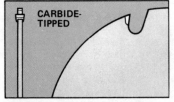

CARBIDE-TIPPED combination blade for long cutting life; ideal for abrasive materials.

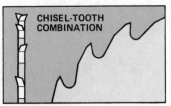

ALL-PURPOSE, fast-cutting blade for all woods. An excellent contractor's framing blade.

Carbide blades —performance at a price

■ YOU MAY NOT need tungsten-carbide-tipped blades for your circular saw. If yours is a light-production workshop, if you rarely work with tough or exotic materials or if you sharpen your own blades regularly, the premium prices of carbide blades probably aren't justifiable.

But if your shop really hums with activity, if you want exceptionally smooth cuts in materials like expensive veneer plywood, or if you've figured the cost of having steel blades sharpened as often as they should be, carbide blades can start to look like a bargain.

They can hustle through materials that mean instant dullness for ordinary steel blades—hardboards, high-pressure laminates and laminated panels, asbestos and soft (nonferrous) metals such as brass and aluminum.

Best of all, they'll stay sharp 10 times longer, on the average, than steel blades will in the same applications. The reason is that tungsten carbide, a manmade substance, is extremely hard—three times harder than the hardened steel used for files.

Not every carbide-tipped blade is right for

every use, of course, and they do suffer from two major disadvantages. The first is high initial cost: Carbide blades commonly cost four or more times as much as the nearest steel equivalents.

The second disadvantage is sharpening—it's costly, too; usually several times as much as commercial sharpening of a comparable steel blade. Don't think you can do it yourself, either—it requires a diamond wheel. If you take a green silicon-carbide wheel to a carbide blade, you're almost certain to wreck the geometry of the tips.

You'll have to work out the cost equation for your own situation. A 10-in. steel blade can be more economical to buy and sharpen than a 24-tip carbide blade after ten sharpenings (which would equal one carbide sharpening). But after that point, the carbide blade quickly becomes more economical.

After half a dozen or more sharpenings, a carbide blade may have lost its clearances (excess carbide that makes it possible to regrind a tip to the correct shape) and will be ready for replacement.

Retipping an entire blade is not economical. It's good to know that if you break one or two blade tips, they can be replaced, however.

In use, the tips of a carbide blade act as tiny chisels, each carrying a chip of material out of the work-piece. A blade's face-rake angle (also called hook angle) determines the angle at which each tip strikes the work. Most carbide blades for home-workshop use have positive rake angles, larger on rip blades and smaller on combination and crosscutting blades.

The way tips are ground also helps to determine a blade's characteristics. Square grind is usually for ripping; alternate top bevel (ATB) is for combination and crosscut blades. Grinds

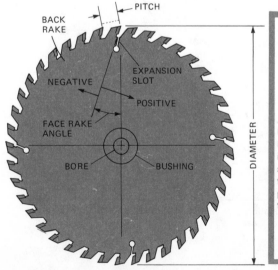

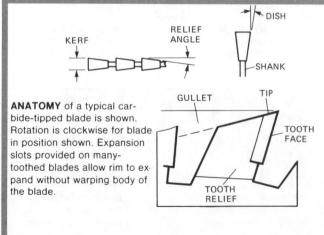

ANATOMY of a typical carbide-tipped blade is shown. Rotation is clockwise for blade in position shown. Expansion slots provided on many-toothed blades allow rim to expand without warping body of the blade.

EIGHT-TIP blade for portable saws does rough carpentry.

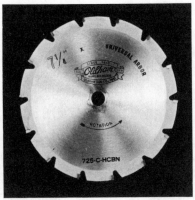

NAIL-CUTTING blade sold by Brookstone has a negative face rake angle.

COMBINATION blade with 20 alternately beveled tips both rips and cross cuts.

SQUARE-GRIND blade is for ripping and rough crosscutting.

LUXITE blade is for radial-arm saws; 12-in., 30-tip model is shown.

FOR ADVANCED woodworking, 10-in.-dia., 60-tip blade cuts silky smooth.

using two ATB tips to one square tip (2-1 or raker grind) and four ATB tips to one square tip are also found on combination and smooth-crosscutting blades. Triple-chip grind (TCG) may also be used on high-grade blades for the do-it-yourselfer, but is not common.

Like most hard materials, tungsten carbide is also brittle. Carbide blades require gentle handling to prevent tip breakage. Keep them in their original packages if possible; if they must be stacked, put cardboard spacers between blades.

It's always important that your saw run true, without play. For true running with minimum wobble, blade makers recommend stabilizers, also called stiffeners. These are discs clamped on both sides of the blade.

Work should be held firmly, clamped when possible. Stop using a carbide blade at the first sign of dullness—tips are easier to break when dull.

As a general rule, the more tips on the blade you choose, the smoother the cut will be—but the sharpening will cost more.

CARBIDE TIP GRINDS (10 and 12-in.-dia. blades)

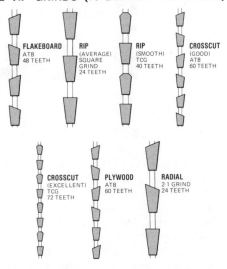

FLAKEBOARD
ATB
48 TEETH

RIP
(AVERAGE)
SQUARE
GRIND
24 TEETH

RIP
(SMOOTH)
TCG
40 TEETH

CROSSCUT
(GOOD)
ATB
60 TEETH

CROSSCUT
(EXCELLENT)
TCG
72 TEETH

PLYWOOD
ATB
60 TEETH

RADIAL
2-1 GRIND
24 TEETH

COMMON GRIND patterns are alternate top bevel (ATB), square, 2-1 (raker) and triple-chip grind (TCG) (is found on the higher-priced blades).

Deburring jig makes saw cut smoother

3/4-IN. PLYWOOD

3/4-IN. PINE CROSSCUT

3/4-IN. CHERRY CROSSCUT

DEBURRING a circular saw blade results in smoother cut edges on all types of wood.

■ YOU'RE PROBABLY NOT getting the smooth cuts you should from your circular saw blades. Even a blade that has just been ground or filed properly has a residual burr that chews up edges and leaves a rough-cut surface. This burr can be eliminated with a jig to give saw blades a final dressing. Dimensions must suit the saw-blade diameter you use.

Blades must be absolutely free of gum and pitch before deburring. The stones are not oiled. The jig is intended for use only with blades that have no set (those with a set do not require deburring). It produces excellent results with ply-

wood blades and combination blades.

It's essential to use a regular (commercial) saw arbor, which must be mounted so that it is at exactly 90° to the stone-carrying slide, in both horizontal and vertical planes. The arbor is secured with a blunt-tipped Phillips-head screw, turned just snug, as a setscrew; the cap atop the post hides the screwhead. A suitable handle is attached to the rear of the arbor.

Bevel natural stones to allow easy insertion of blades between them. Use glue sparingly when attaching the stones. Allow complete drying between gluing operations to keep foam spongy.

EL TOOL separates foam-sprung
~s for insertion of saw blade, is kept in
pool at rear of jig.

SLIDE IS PINNED into place with blade between stones. Pin is mounted in cutoff
thread spool attached with cord keeper.

BLADE gets five or six turns between soft
stones first, in direction *counter* to that in
which it normally cuts.

ER ANOTHER half-dozen turns be-
n hard stones, blade is turned against
r on block to test for smoothness.

CUTTING OR SCRATCHES on paper surface indicate that deburring is incomplete
and that process must be repeated.

STONES MEASURE 3/8 x 7/8 x 3 in., are lightly
glued to 3/8-in. polyurethane foam blocks
lightly glued to slide.

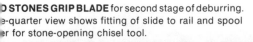

D STONES GRIP BLADE for second stage of deburring.
e-quarter view shows fitting of slide to rail and spool
r for stone-opening chisel tool.

WINGNUTS FASTEN REAR FACE of slide in place, so it can
be removed when stones must be replaced. Front face
attaches to center piece with three Phillips-head screws.

WEAR
SAFETY
GOGGLES

Portable saw bench you can build

COMPLETED TABLE boasts miter gauge, fence and a sawdust clean-out drawer. It can be easily carried to job site (above). Following photos show how to build it.

■ GET TWICE as much work from your portable circular saw by building this table that lets you convert it for use as a stationary unit. With the aid of an adjustable fence and miter gauge you make, this rig lets you make accurate rips and angled crosscuts quickly. When you have

TO MAKE cutouts in the plywood for various bench parts, drill holes at corners and then use a sabre saw guided by a tacked-down straightedge.

POSITION SAW on table underside using a straight-edge along side of blade. It should be parallel to table sides and perpendicular to front.

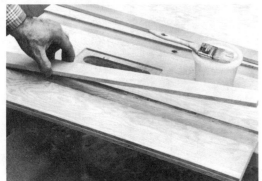

FOR LONG-WEARING miter-gauge grooves, glue maple inserts (U) in table recesses. Use a router with a mortising bit to cut these grooves.

USE GLUE and 1½-in. finishing nails to assemble the sides. Be sure to check for squareness. Set the nails with a nailset and then fill the holes.

CUT TABLE INSERT recess using a router and mortising bit. Wood strips tacked to the plywood act as a guide for the base of the router.

DEPENDING on the angle or range of angles required to cut a particular bevel, one of four inserts is used to reduce the cutout width.

need for a portable saw, simply detach it from the table underside.

The on-off switch is mounted on the table front to let you control the saw from the operating position. Use a length of wire or electrician's tape wrapped around the saw's trigger and handle grip to secure it in the ON position.

The main design problem for any portable saw table is providing enough clearance for the saw to tilt and cut bevels—without making the cutout opening for the blade and guard so wide that it would pose a hazard when cutting small pieces of wood. The problem is solved here by making a series of four blade inserts of ¼-in. plywood. The

DETAIL OF TOP A

4-1/8" 2" 8" 2"

7-7/8"

10-1/2"

8-1/4"

4"

3/8 x 2" GROOVE
(2 PLACES)
FOR INSERT U

5-3/8"

20"

1/4"-DIA. HOLE AND
COUNTERSINK FOR
MOUNTING SAW
WITH 1/4"-20- x 1"
FH SCREW AND
NUT (2 REQD.)

X

1-9/16"

2"

A

1/4 x 3 x 8-3/4"
RECESS FOR
BLADE INSERTS

4"

4"

9-3/4"

19-7/8"

SAW-CUTOUT DETAIL

1/4"

5/8"

3-1/4"

7-1/2"

1/4"

1/8"

3/4"

1"

1-5/8"

ACTUAL SAW CUTOUT

BLADE-INSERT DETAILS

| 5/8" | 1" | 3/4" |
| 3-1/4" | M | 3-1/8" |

1"

5/8"

1-3/8"

INSERT 1
0° - 15° TILT

1-1/4"

M

3-1/2"

3-1/8"

3/4"

3/4"

INSERT 2
16° - 27° TILT

1-1/8"

M

3-1/2"

3-1/8"

3/4"

1/2"

INSERT 3
28° - 36° TILT

1-1/2"

M

3-5/8"

2-1/2"

3/4"

1/2"

INSERT 4
37° - 45° TILT

DETAIL PIECE V

2-1/4"

V

1-3/8"

U

1"

1/2"

3/8"

U

W

Y

M

A

DRILL HOLE AND INSTALL
1/4" TEENUT (4 PLACES)

1/4"-DIA. HOLE,
COUNTERSINK
(4 PLACES)

CC

GG

EE

DD

BB

V

FF

2-1/4 x 4"
CUTOUT

2"

10-1/8"

6"

2"

2-7/16"

19-7/8"

20"

2-7/16"

2"

2-7/16"

R

E

Q

KNOT
WIRE

E

D

Z

O

O

8"

11"

L

P

K

11"

L

K

2"

HH

1/2"

3/4"

4-3/4"

5-3/4"

16-13/16"

B

18-3/4"

1/2"

2"

II

2"

S

G

S

C

2"

3/4"

31/32"

31/32"

12"

17-7/8"

D

F

G

3/4"-DIA.
HOLE

C

3/8"

5"

2"

N

F

G

GG

C

POWER-
SUPPLY
CORD

I

J

H

J

5"

N

D

1/8"

N

2"

AA

B

T

I

1-1/2"

3/4"

8"

3"

5-1/4"

N

DRAWER ASSEMBLY

G

2"

S

5-3/4"

F

3-1/2"

S

ASSEMBLE TABLE
WITH 1-1/2"
FINISHING
NAILS AND GLUE

8"

1/2"

TABLE ASSEMBLY

H

F

M

J

H

F

1/2"

O

E

N

G

O

G

I

I

C

C

D

D

DRILL AND TAP
FOR 1/4"- 20
THREADS

DETAIL PIECE O

FENCE-SECTION VIEWS

FENCE ASSEMBLY

E

L

Q

R

K P

J

H

N

I

M

O

G

F

C

D

3/4"

3/16"

1/4"

3/4"

1-1/2"

M

3/8"-
DIA.
HOLE

DETAIL PIECE M

W

T

V

A

3"
RADIUS

90°

4"
RADIUS

3/8"
SLOT

1-1/4"

DRILL AND TAP
FOR 1/4"- 20
THREADS

MITER-GAUGE ASSEMBLY

1/4"-DIA. HOLE

B X

S

U

3"

1/4"-DIA. HOLE,
COUNTERSINK
ON BOTTOM

MATERIALS LIST—SAW TABLE

Key	No.	Size and description (use)
A	1	¾ × 28 × 36" plywood (top)
B	1	¾ × 5¾ × 18¾" plywood (drawer face)
C	2	½ × 22⅞ × 34" plywood (front, back)
D	2	½ × 24⅞ × 34" plywood (side)
E	4	½ × 5½ × 5½" plywood (corner blocks)
F	4	½ × 2 × 6" plywood (drawer supports)
G	2	½ × 6 × 23⅞" plywood (drawer supports)
H	1	⅜ × 16¹³/₁₆ × 23½" plywood (drawer bottom)
I	2	⅜ × 4⅜ × 23½" plywood (drawer sides)
J	2	⅜ × 4⅜ × 16¹/₁₆" plywood (drawer ends)
K	2	¼ × 4¼ × 22⅞" plywood (sawdust-shield ends)
L	2	¼ × 4¼ × 23⅞" plywood (sawdust-shield sides)
M	4	¼ × 3 × 8¾" lauan plywood (blade inserts)
N	4	1½ × 1½ × 8" fir (glue blocks)
O	2	¾ × ¾ × 22⅞" pine (cleats)
P	1	¾ × ¾ × 23⅛" pine (cleat)
Q	1	¾ × ¾ × 4¾" pine (cleat)
R	1	¾ × ¾ × 8" pine (cleat)
S	4	½ × ¾ × 23⅞" pine (drawer guide)
T	2	½ × ¾ × 23½" pine (drawer guide)
U	2	⅜ × 2 × 28" maple (tabletop inserts)
V	1	2⅛ × 3¼ × 6" fir (outlet-box support block)
W	4	¼"-20 × 1½" fh machine screw and Teenut
X	2	¼"-dia. × 1" fh machine screw
Y	2	¾" No. 6 fh screw
Z	4	1" brad
AA	1	drawer pull
BB	1	outlet box
CC	2	½" No. 8 fh screw
DD	2	cable clamp
EE	1	single-pole switch
FF	1	single receptacle and short length of No. 12 wire with ground
GG	1	6' or to suit, 3' lead wire and male plug
HH	1	switch plate
II	2	1½" No. 10 fh screw

Misc.: 1½" finishing nails and glue as required.

MATERIALS LIST—FENCE MITER GAUGE

Key	No.	Size and description (use)
A	1	¾ × 5 × 8" plywood (miter quadrant)
B	1	¾ × 2½ × 10" plywood (miter-gauge face)
C	1	¾ × 4½ × 5¼" plywood (fence head)
D	1	¾ × 5¼ × 5½" plywood (fence head)
E	1	⅜ × 3⅜ × 33½" plywood (fence face)
F	1	⅜ × 3 × 33½" plywood (fence back)
G	1	⅜ × 3 × 31¾" plywood (fence bottom)
H	1	¾ × ¾ × 31¼" pine (fence core)
I	1	¾ × ¾ × 31" pine (fence core)
J	1	¾ × ¾ × 3" pine (fence core)
K	1	¾ × ¾ × 1½" pine (fence core)
L	1	¾ × 1½ × 4½" pine (fence clamping toe)
M	1	¾ × 1½ × 4" pine (fence clamping cam)
N	1	¼"-20 × 34¾" threaded rod (fence hardware)
O	1	⅜" dia. × 1" steel rod (fence hardware)
P	1	¹¹/₁₆" dia. × 1¼" compression spring (fence)
Q	1	¼" I.D. rubber grommet (fence hardware)
R	2	¼"-20 nut
S	1	¼ × 1 × 16" aluminum bar (miter-guage hardware)
T	1	¼" dia. × 1" aluminum rivet (miter-gauge)
U	1	¼"-20 x 1¼" threaded rod (miter-gauge)
V	1	¼" I.D., ¾" O.D. flat washer (miter-gauge)
W	1	¼"-20 wingnut (miter-gauge hardware)
X	2	¾" no. 10 fh screw

Misc.: 1" brads and glue as required.

odd configuration of the inserts is due to changing blade-guard positions at various blade heights and tilt combinations.

This portable saw table was dimensioned for a J. C. Penney Model 1125 7¼-in. saw. If you have a different model, change inserts to suit. Make cardboard patterns to work out shapes.

The easiest way to build the table is to cut all parts and then preassemble the sawdust clean-out drawer supports (F, G and S). After assembling the sides, install drawer supports by nailing from the outside.

Four corner blocks (E) are used to anchor the tabletop to the sides. They should be temporarily nailed to the supporting cleats so mounting holes can be bored through top (A) and blocks (B) simultaneously. Remove the blocks to install Teenuts before gluing them permanently.

Aligning the saw with the table is critical. After making the cutout in A, locate the saw mounting holes to correspond to those provided on your saw shoe. If holes are not provided, you will have to drill them. Align the blade with the sides of the squared table; do not use the edge of the saw shoe. Then mark and bore holes for ¼-20 fh machine screws. Countersink for screwheads.

Note that the stepped patterns on the right sides of the inserts are important. They hold the guard partly raised and let it be pushed back as work is fed toward the blade.

One fence-assembly step that may give you trouble is attaching the fence's cam lock (M) to the threaded rod (N). To attach, bore a hole in a length of ⅜-in. steel rod using a drill press and clamp to hold the work. Tap ¼-in.-20 threads in the hole and cut the rod to size. Insert the piece (O) through holes in sides of cam lock and screw in the rod (H).

When the table is complete, the base may be painted. The top should be finished with two coats of satin varnish, lightly rubbed with 000 steel wool and coated with silicone lubricant or wax.

SINGLE-POLE switch is connected between power-supply cord (GG) and pigtail (FF). Saw plugs into receptacle.

CAREFUL CONSTRUCTION of fence (part E removed to show assembly) and miter gauge assures accurate cuts.

Clamp selection and use

THE PROPER clamps and a few blocks of wood make even the most difficult-to-hold joints, such as these curves, easy to glue.

■ WHETHER IT'S ACTUATED by a screw, toggle or cam mechanism, a clamp has one prime function—to squeeze. Keep this in mind when searching among the clamps available commercially, and you'll find that the selection of the right clamp for your shop or the job at hand will depend upon the size and the type of material to be squeezed or compressed.

Compression has three common uses in shopwork. Clamping glued joints is one. Securing stock to be worked with power tools is another. The third is the clamping together of temporarily assembled jigs and fixtures.

For all these jobs, compression in the range of 100 to 200 lbs. is required. This is the optimum clamping pressure for glued joints. It's sufficient pressure to hold clamped-down work firmly and safely, and to keep jigs from slipping or sliding.

General purpose clamps, special clamps

The many different shop clamps used to apply this compression—without damaging or marring the work—can be grouped into two classes: general-purpose clamps for most jobs and special clamps for specific jobs.

C-clamps, handscrews and short-bar clamps are three useful general-purpose clamps that you should have in your shop. C-clamps (termed G-clamps in England) are so useful in everyday shopwork that they are considered basic hand tools. With enough of them—together with lengths of scrap lumber, blocks and wedges— you can easily improvise clamping setups for just about any job.

Most moderately-priced C-clamps have frames of malleable iron, while top-quality clamps have frames of drop-forged steel, heat-treated Acme-threaded screws and smoothly machined ball-swivel pads for the greatest strength and performance.

Frame patterns also differ. Standard-pattern clamps are fine for many jobs, but have a limited depth-of-throat. Both malleable iron and forged steel clamps are available in deep-throat patterns that will prove well worth their extra cost.

Large C-clamps can apply considerable pressure, but because the pressure is applied in one spot, you should always use strips of scrap wood to distribute the pressure evenly. If you're clamping wood, this will prevent the clamp pads from compressing and denting the surface.

Handscrews, for centuries the clamps preferred by fine-furniture craftsmen, have parallel jaws made of straight-grain hard maple. When properly adjusted, the oil-finished jaws apply the pressure evenly over a broad area to grip tightly without marring the work. After you've caught the knack, you'll find that you can adjust a handscrew very quickly by grasping the handles and swinging the jaws around the spindles. Screwing the outer spindle develops leverage and tightens

SHORT-BAR CLAMP with disc-clutch sliding head is modern descendant of the old-time iron ratchet clamp.

MAPLE-JAW handscrews offer the inherent advantage of distributing clamping pressure over a broad area.

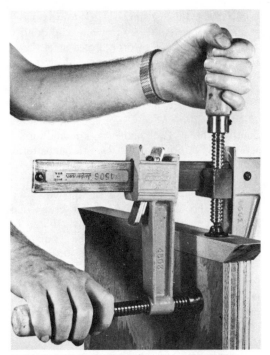

EDGE-CLAMP FIXTURES are auxiliary screws that attach to bar clamps, apply pressure at a right angle.

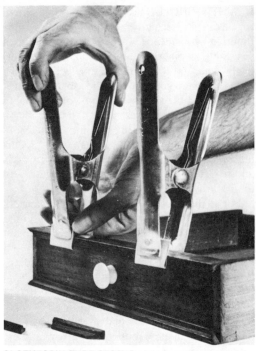

CLOTHESPIN-TYPE SPRING clamps apply adequate pressure for small gluing jobs, positioning of parts.

LONG CLAMPS for edge-gluing strips of lumber can be made of ¾-in. pipe and commercial clamp fixtures.

ALUMINUM-ALLOY corner clamps are handy for gluing mitered joints in frames made of light stock.

UNIVERSAL MITER clamp has two screws that grip halves of miter joint and a third screw to tighten the joint.

SPRING CLAMP has pivoting jaws, needle-sharp teeth to grip wood. Masking tape minimizes tooth marks.

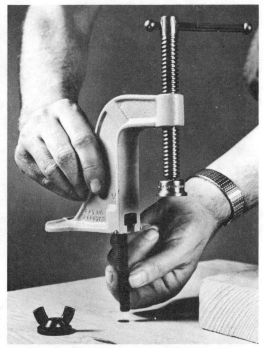

HOLD-DOWN CLAMP for benchtop requires drilling hole in top, inserting clamp and tightening the wingnut.

BLOCK-AND-WEDGE JIG is easy setup for gluing 90° joints. Nail blocks to scrap plywood, tap in wedges.

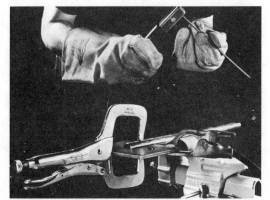

TOGGLE CLAMPS grip tightly without twisting work. Quick-release model above aids in welding, brazing.

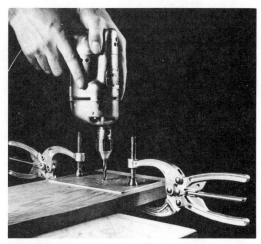

TRIGGER-RELEASE CLAMP is handy for securing metal stock to be worked safely with portable power tools.

the jaws which, in turn, should always grip the work squarely.

A handscrew's depth-of-throat is half its jaw length. Commonly available are handscrews with jaws 4 to 24 in. long. Most cabinetmakers find that the 12-in. size (No. 2) ordinarily is the most useful.

Short-bar clamps, which essentially are quick-adjusting C-clamps, are also excellent general-woodworking clamps. The newer types have disc-clutch screwheads that slide on heavy spring-steel bars. Top-quality models have a depth-of-throat of 5 in. and capacities beginning at 6 in.

These three standbys—C-clamps, handscrews, and short-bar clamps—will take care of almost any common clamping job you're likely to encounter, provided you use enough of them. Clamping generally requires the application of evenly distributed pressure over the entire gluing surface. Thus, because you'll need a clamp every 8 to 12 in. along a long joint, a number of clamps should be kept in your shop. You just can't have too many.

Other woodworking clamps

There are three other clamps you might find useful for common woodworking jobs. The first is a long-bar clamp, especially useful for edge-gluing and cabinet assembly. The second is a half-C-clamp that bolts through a benchtop to hold down work firmly. The third is a short-bar clamp with a hinged foot that screws under the edge of a benchtop.

Bar clamps you can make

■ THESE LIGHTWEIGHT, quick-acting bar clamps are ideal for woodworking where only moderate pressure is needed to hold the joint. The clamping action is produced by a toggle linkage which snaps past center to exert force. To operate the clamp you bring the handle forward and slide the movable jaw against the work. Then you pull the handle back with one hand and adjust the locking jaw with the other until sufficient force is applied to the work. Finally, you pull the handle all the way back to lock the clamp. This causes the locking jaw to bite into the bar.

The three jaws required for each clamp (movable, fixed and locking) are formed from hot-rolled strip steel and are bent around a hardwood form clamped in a vice. The steel strip is clamped to the block with a C-clamp and bent by hand around the end. Notice that the bending point is 1⅝ in. from the center point of the strip. You can use a tension pin in the movable jaw, but a No. 10 machine screw will do. You could also silver-solder the parts with a butane torch, or they could be welded.

Common ¾-in. thinwall conduit is used for the bars and they can be made any length you want up to 10 ft. The fixed jaw is silver-soldered to the end of the bar, while the others are free to slide along it. Bike handlebar grips can be added to the clamp handles.

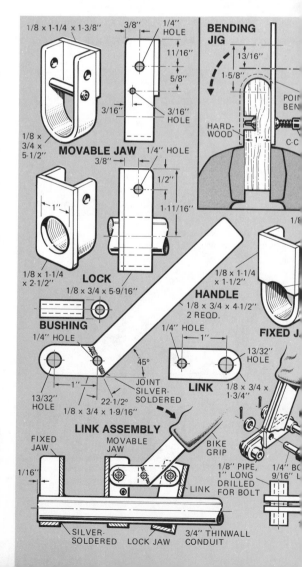

Machine-vise clamp

■ HERE'S AN EASY way to clamp a drill-press vise on a T-slotted table without interfering with the work in the vise jaws. It's called a two-way machine-vise clamp and is operated either by a simple screw or a screw-operated wedge that's quick acting and requires no wrench.

The essential clamp components include the steel block that acts as a lever; a ½-20 bolt that serves as the fulcrum; a sliding wedge, and a lathe-turned teenut threaded on the ½-20 bolt. The wedge slides along the bottom of the table slot and is applied or retracted by turning the long threaded rod engaging the threaded hole

A SCREW or wedge can easily apply enough clamping force to hold a machine vise; flat pieces of stock; wide or odd-shaped sections that are too awkward for the vise alone. When holding flat work, shims usually are necessary.

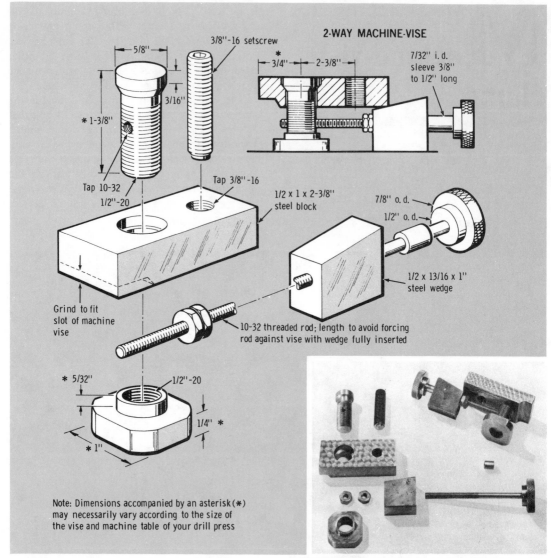

2-WAY MACHINE-VISE

3/8"-16 setscrew

5/8"

3/16"

* 1-3/8"

Tap 10-32

1/2"-20

Tap 3/8"-16

7/32" i. d. sleeve 3/8" to 1/2" long

* 3/4" — 2-3/8"

1/2 x 1 x 2-3/8" steel block

7/8" o. d.

1/2" o. d.

1/2 x 13/16 x 1" steel wedge

Grind to fit slot of machine vise

10-32 threaded rod; length to avoid forcing rod against vise with wedge fully inserted

* 5/32"

1/2"-20

1/4" *

* 1"

Note: Dimensions accompanied by an asterisk (*) may necessarily vary according to the size of the vise and machine table of your drill press

MAKE TWO of each piece to produce a pair of these clamps. Above, they're ready for assembly.

through the ½-20 bolt. The collar between the knurled knob and the wedge serves to position the knob so it falls outside the table slot.

For these parts, you can use either hardenable tool steel or cold-rolled steel, case-hardened where maximum wear resistance is required. The head of the ½-20 bolt should be turned so it is a loose fit in the counterbored hole in the steel block. Similarly, the hole for the long threaded rod through the sliding wedge should be large enough to pass the rod freely. The two locknuts on this rod serve to withdraw the wedge when the rod is backed out of its hole in the ½-20 bolt.

The alternate method of applying the clamping force requires an additional threaded hole (⅜-16) in the steel block. Through this extends a matching bolt long enough to press against the bottom of the table slot, but short enough to keep from projecting above the top of the block. This arrangement is compact and provides good clamping force—but a wrench is required to tighten or loosen the clamp, and the hollow-head screw will tend to fill with metal chips that interfere with the wrench.

As noted, the specific dimensions in the drawing are for the clamps shown.

Connecticut shelf clock

■ AS A PROJECT, this clock has just about everything to recommend it to the home craftsman. The styling is authentic, construction is simple and the cost is surprisingly low.

The clock shown is fitted with an eight-day short-pendulum movement and a roman-numeral dial. If you would prefer to eliminate the ticking and the necessity of having to wind the clock once a week, a battery-powered electric movement could be substituted.

The original Connecticut shelf clocks (or "mirror clocks," as they were sometimes called) were made with a variety of different door panels. Some had a small mirror, while others used hand-painted scenes. When they were fitted with pendulum movements, however, a small oval area was always left clear so the pendulum action could be seen.

You can get the effect of a hand-painted scene with a piece of wallpaper cut from a sample roll at the local paint store. Simply glue this to the back of a clear glass panel.

You can use common white pine since it is considered authentic for this type of clock, but many New England clocks had cases of cherry, mahogany or walnut.

The sides and top of the case require a piece of wood ¾ in. thick, 4 in. wide and approximately 30 in. long. Run the front and rear rabbets along the sides of the piece before cutting it up into specific lengths. It is best to sand it first, using No. 80 grit paper and then No. 220.

The sides are joined to the top piece by a joint called a rabbet-miter, which you'll find makes a strong joint and simplifies the job of clamping. To cut such a joint, you first set the blade on your table saw ⁵⁄₁₆ in. high. Then you set the fence so it's ¾ in. from the outside of the blade. Make the cut across the end of both side pieces first, then shift the fence so you can make a second cut halfway from the end of the pieces. The area between the cuts is cleaned out with two or three passes. Now set the fence ⁷⁄₁₆ in. from the outside of the blade and make a cut across both ends of the top piece. With this done, set the blade at 45° and miter each end. The miter cut should just reach the root of the first cut. Finally, make similar miter cuts at the upper ends of the side pieces. You can now trim the side pieces to 9¾ in.

The next step is to glue the miter joints and clamp them. A temporary spreader piece across the bottom of the assembly will ensure square corners. It's best to use a scrap at the bottom now so that any variation in width at the top caused by clamping can be compensated for by cutting the final bottom piece. Fasten this piece with glue and 6d finishing nails.

Next, rip a 20-in.-long piece for the three base pieces. Use your molding head to round the top edge, or form it with a hand plane and sandpaper. Cut the strip into three pieces and miter them to fit around three sides of the case at the bottom. In doing this, the important thing to remember is that the inner face of the front piece must extend the full width of the clock case. The side pieces of the base are left extra long for final trimming after the miters are checked for a good fit. Drive small brads into the case at the bottom and cut the heads off so they impale the base and prevent shifting when gluing and clamping.

Screwing the hardboard back to the case completes the job. Use ½-in. No. 6 oval or flathead screws to fasten it in the rabbets.

Simple butt joints are used to make the door. Rabbet the members for the two pieces of glass, then glue the door together. After the glue dries, run saw kerfs in the joints at the corners and insert splines. Fit the door to the case so there is ¹⁄₃₂-in. clearance at top and bottom and ¹⁄₁₆-in. at the sides. The hinges are mortised into the edge of the door but not into the case. Use only one screw in each leaf for a trial fit. Then you can

THE CLOCK MOVEMENT is a standard eight-day short-pendulum type which has a roman-numeral dial.

CUT BOTH RABBETS in one 30-in. board. Then cut the sides and top to length from this board.

THE RABBET MITER used to join the sides and top is begun by making a ⁵⁄₁₆-inch cut ¾ inch from the end.

A SECOND CUT more than halfway to the end is then made and the area between the cuts is cleaned.

A MITER CUT at 45° should just reach the first cut. Sides are cut to length.

THE SIDES AND TOP are glued together after miter cuts have been made.

make an adjustment if necessary.

Fasten the glass in the upper section of the door temporarily with a couple of brads. Then cut 3 and 6-in. squares of ⅛-in. hardboard. Locate the holes for the hand shaft and key stem in the 6-in. piece by using the dial plate as a pattern. Now center the 3-in. square and glue it to the rear face of the 6-in. square. This double thickness is needed since the threaded bushings supplied with most movements are designed for ¼-in. panels.

For best visibility, the clock hands should be located as close as possible to the glass. First, fas-

ten the movement to the 6-in. square and measure the projection of the minute-hand shaft. Then add 5/32 in. to the dimension, close the door and measure in to locate the support cleats which are attached to each side of the case. Fasten the cleats only temporarily, place the movement in position with the case on its back and check the clearance between the glass and the shaft. Finally, remove the cleats, apply glue and fasten them permanently.

After stripping off the metal frame and using just the magnet and the two pole plates, use a

GLUE AND NAIL the mitered joints with 6d finishing nails. Blunt the nail points to avoid splitting.

BRAD POINTS keep the base pieces from shifting when gluing. Drive them part way, then cut off the heads.

TIGHTEN THE CLAMPS slowly and evenly so as not to force the mitered corners out of line; apply as shown.

THE BACK OF THE CASE fits flush in rabbets previously cut in the top and sides. The back laps the bottom.

AFTER GLUING the butt corners of the door frame, ⅛-in. splines are inserted, glued and trimmed flush.

HINGE MORTISES are cut in the frame only. Make approximately 1/16-in. deep to assure proper clearance.

THE MOVEMENT is mounted on the dial backing plate, then used to determine the location of the support.

A MAGNETIC CATCH, stripped of its frame, is fastened to the case with a screw through the center hole.

A STRIP OF PAPER is used to check minimum clearance between the minute-hand shaft and the glass.

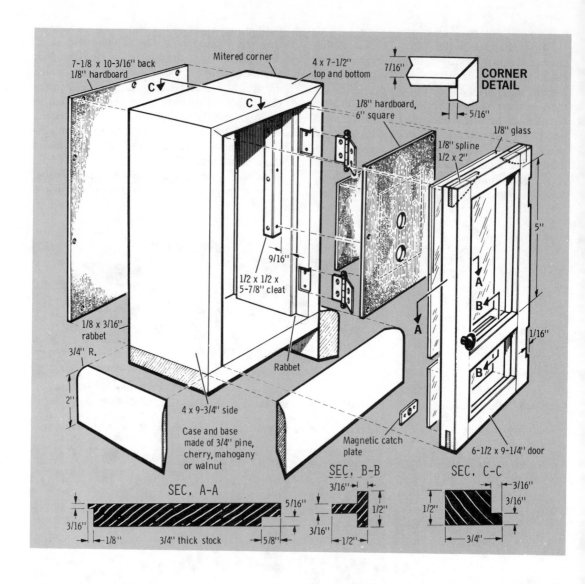

CORNER DETAIL

7-1/8 x 10-3/16" back 1/8" hardboard

Mitered corner

4 x 7-1/2" top and bottom

7/16"

5/16"

1/8" hardboard, 6" square

1/8" spline 1/2 x 2"

1/8" glass

9/16"

1/2 x 1/2 x 5-7/8" cleat

5"

1/8 x 3/16" rabbet

3/4" R.

2"

Rabbet

Magnetic catch plate

4 x 9-3/4" side

Case and base made of 3/4" pine, cherry, mahogany or walnut

1/16"

6-1/2 x 9-1/4" door

SEC. A-A

5/16"

3/16"

1/8"

3/4" thick stock

5/8"

SEC. B-B

3/16"

1/2"

3/16"

1/2"

SEC. C-C

3/16"

3/16"

1/2"

3/4"

magnetic catch to hold the door shut.

If you'd like to finish your clock as shown, brush on pigmented wiping stain, a 50/50 mixture of walnut and French provincial. Let stand until it starts to flatten, then wipe with a cloth. Let dry 24 hours. Next apply a coat of color glaze. Wipe off with a cloth, leaving traces in the corners, nicks and scratches. Let dry 24 to 48 hours. Follow with two coats of sanding sealer, letting them dry an hour or so between coats. Now sand *lightly* with 6/0 garnet paper and dust thoroughly. Next brush on four coats of lacquer, allowing 30 minutes between coats. Let dry 24 hours.

Wet-sand with soapy water and No. 400 wet-or-dry paper on a felt or rubber block. Use light pressure and inspect the surface frequently by wiping. Stop sanding when the surface has an even satin finish and clean up with a dry cloth.

Fasten the dial backing plate to the support cleats with 1/2-in. No. 4 flathead screws, drop the dial plate into position and install the movement with bushings. Always remember to remove the pendulum before moving the clock.

If you choose a hand-wound movement for your clock, you may want to put a small hook on the back of the case. Use it to keep the key from getting lost between windings.

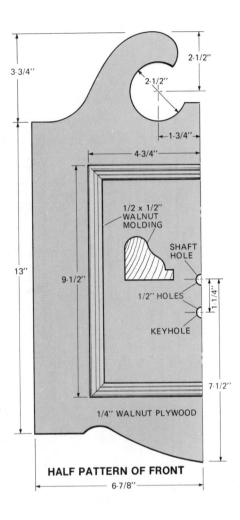

3-3/4"

2-1/2"

2-1/2"

1-3/4"

4-3/4"

1/2 x 1/2"
WALNUT
MOLDING

SHAFT
HOLE

13"

9-1/2"

1/2" HOLES

1-1/4"

KEYHOLE

7-1/2"

1/4" WALNUT PLYWOOD

HALF PATTERN OF FRONT

6-7/8"

Heirloom wall clock

■ IF THERE IS SOMEONE on your gift list who would like a fine clock, he'll be delighted with this handsome wall model—especially when he knows you made it. Its elegant, etched dial and spun-brass pendulum contrast beautifully with its walnut case.

Other than the ¼-in. veneer-faced plywood, you'll probably find most of the wood in your scrap box. In the case of the three-sided frame, only the side members need to be walnut since the top piece is not exposed. The two split pilasters are produced from a single square turning by gluing two pieces of wood together with paper between. Once turned, the two halves are easily pried apart with a knife blade down the paper joint. Use a fine-tooth blade to jigsaw the plywood parts and carefully sand the edges. If you have a router, you can run your own molding, or make use of a suitable stock picture-frame molding.

Specialty stores sell the eight-day windup movement, dial and brass finial. You also can buy a kit of partially cut wood parts, including preturned pilasters.

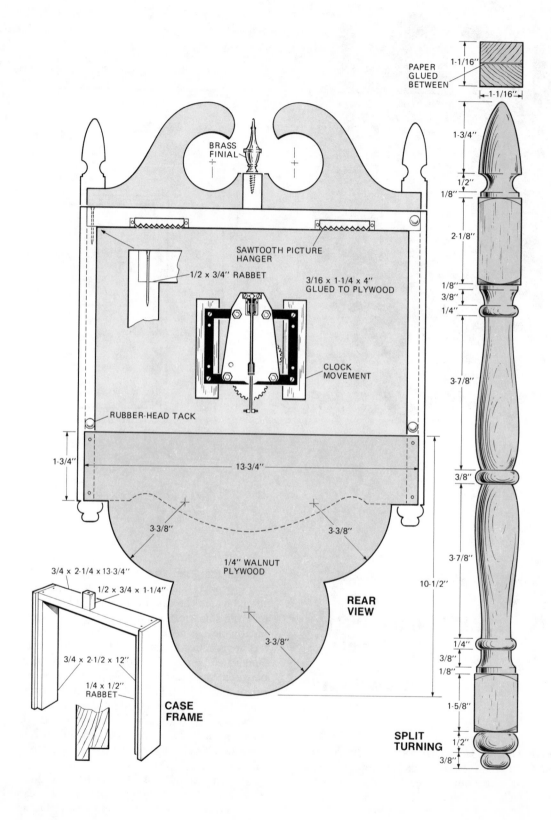

PAPER
GLUED
BETWEEN

1-1/16"

1-1/16"

BRASS
FINIAL

1-3/4"

1/2"

1/8"

2-1/8"

1/8"

3/8"

1/4"

SAWTOOTH PICTURE
HANGER

1/2 x 3/4" RABBET

3/16 x 1-1/4 x 4"
GLUED TO PLYWOOD

3-7/8"

CLOCK
MOVEMENT

RUBBER-HEAD TACK

3/8"

1-3/4"

13-3/4"

3-3/8"

3-3/8"

1/4" WALNUT
PLYWOOD

3-7/8"

10-1/2"

**REAR
VIEW**

3/4 x 2-1/4 x 13-3/4"

1/2 x 3/4 x 1-1/4"

3/4 x 2-1/2 x 12"

1/4 x 1/2"
RABBET

**CASE
FRAME**

3-3/8"

1/4"

3/8"

1/8"

1-5/8"

**SPLIT
TURNING**

1/2"

3/8"

Wall clock from your lathe

■ HERE'S A GIFT you can literally turn out by the dozen. It requires a lathe, but once you have made the workholding jig, you can practically mass produce these handsome wall clocks. You buy the ceramic dial and clock works and make and finish the wooden face from fancy ¼-in. plywood. The jig serves as a large faceplate to which you attach the work for turning a recess and decorative grooves. It consists of an 11¼-in. disc cut from ¾-in. plywood and fitted with four ¼ x 1¼-in. roundhead stovebolts and wingnuts. The bolts automatically center the work, while their heads clamp it to the jig which is mounted on the lathe by a regular faceplate.

The work is cut octagon-shape before it is attached to the jig. If you plan to make more than one clock, each piece should be identical to fit the jig.

Specialty stores sell the ceramic dial and clock. You have a choice of dial designs and a battery or electric movement.

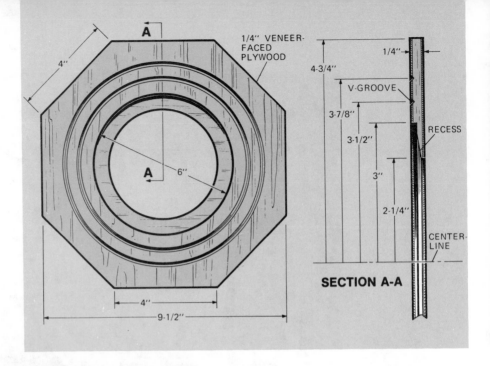

**PATTERN FOR
CLOCK FACE**

1/4" VENEER-
FACED
PLYWOOD

4"

6"

4"

9-1/2"

A

A

SECTION A-A

1/4"

V-GROOVE

RECESS

CENTER-
LINE

4-3/4"

3-7/8"

3-1/2"

3"

2-1/4"

WINGNUTS ON BOLTS make it easy to clamp the work to face side of the plywood disc. Faceplate fastens disc.

BOLT HEADS grip the edge of the work, holding it as you turn dial recess and decorative grooves in the face.

CONTACT CEMENT is used to glue 6-in. ceramic dial in the turned recess. Apply adhesive to dial and recess.

TWO WOOD CLEATS, ¾ x 1 x 6 in., are glued to the back of the facing to gain clearance for the clock.

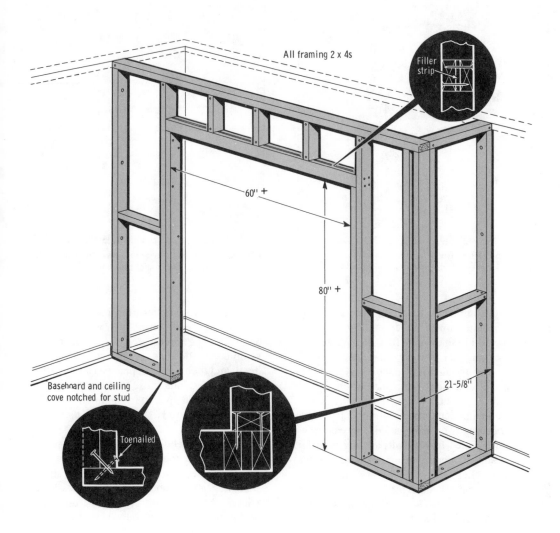

All framing 2 x 4s

Filler strip

60" +

80" +

21-5/8"

Baseboard and ceiling cove notched for stud

Toenailed

Closets you can build in

■ FEW HOMEOWNERS can boast of having too many closets. More often it's a case of not having enough. The solution, of course, is to add another.

While the thought of building an extra closet could cause the less experienced home remodeler to turn and run, it's not the major job it seems. Actually, a good share of the task is rough work, particularly the framing. As to where to put it, usually there's a corner that will give up 20 in. or so without it being missed a bit. And as for it looking like a "sore thumb," you can see in the drawings that such a closet adds considerable eye appeal.

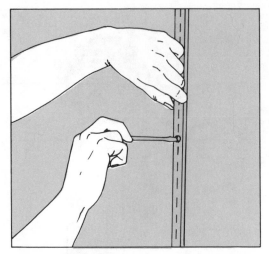

SLOTTED STANDARDS, 5 ft. long, are screwed to the studs in the back wall of the closet for solid support.

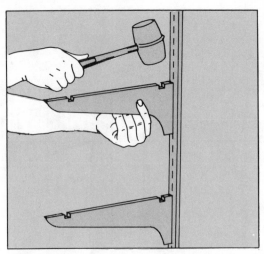

TABS ON the brackets hook in slots of the standards and a tap of a hammer or mallet locks them in place.

The length and depth you make the closet is up to you. The one shown is made shallow so it will accept six 16-in. shelves, 8 ft. long. While the overall size can vary to suit your needs, the size given for the rough door opening should be maintained if you use standard-size 15-in. bifold doors. Here the actual width and height of the rough opening is determined beforehand by the way the opening is to be trimmed. For example, if ¼-in. prefinished hardboard paneling is to be used, the rough opening is made ½ in. greater than the finished width of 60 in., and ¼ in. greater than the finished height of 80 in. If, on the other hand, you plan to face the walls with plasterboard and trim the opening in the conventional manner with ¾-in. jambs and casings, the rough opening would have to measure 61½ in. wide and 80¾ in. high.

Your first step after plotting the closet's size on the floor is to cut out 4-in. sections of the existing baseboard so the framing will butt tight where it joins the wall. When this is done, 2x4 plates are nailed to both the floor and ceiling, fastening the ceiling ones first so they can be used in locating the floor plates directly below. A plumb line dropped from the top plates will spot the exact position of the floor plates quickly.

Whether you have anything to which to nail the ceiling plates depends on the direction the ceiling joists run. If they cross the top plate at right angles, you're in luck. If they don't, a few toggle bolts will do the trick. The same holds true in fastening the vertical framing members to the walls. Chances are they won't fall directly on a stud for nailing.

Once the top and bottom plates are in place, it's now a case of cutting the 2x4 studs to wedge between. The three-piece corner post is preassembled in the manner shown in the circular detail and then nailed in place as a unit. All studs are toe-nailed, and those framing the door opening are doubled up in the manner shown. Keep in mind that the studs should be placed 16 in. on centers.

We used prefinished hardboard paneling to cover the studs to match the paneling which was already there. The detailed drawings show how matching metal molding is used to add a neat trim to the hardboard around the door opening and to both inside and outside corners.

In using hardboard (and the same procedure is followed in using plywood paneling), you first line the door opening with strips of paneling ripped 3½ in. wide. These are cemented with special mastic directly to the studs and headers. Next, outside corner molding is applied around the outer edges of the opening, front and back, by nailing through the flange part of the molding. Note that it's mitered at the corners and nailed every 4 in.

From here on you apply the paneling to the studs and cut it to fit into the grooves of the molding. When you reach the corner, the same molding is applied in the same manner, first hooking it over the paneling, then nailing through the flange and inserting the succeeding piece in the molding as you continue around the corner. Inside corners are trimmed similarly but with molding of a different shape.

If you plan to use plasterboard, study the

HARDBOARD TREATMENT

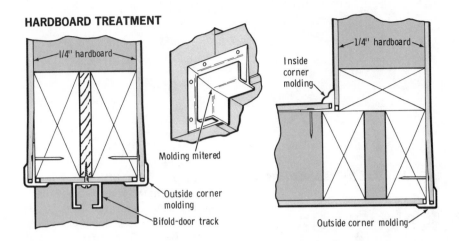

1/4" hardboard

Molding mitered

Outside corner molding

Bifold-door track

Inside corner molding

1/4" hardboard

Outside corner molding

drawings below. Procedure differs in that the door opening is lined with ¾-in. jambs, ripped 4⅝ in. wide, and centered so they project ½ in. each side. The ½-in. plasterboard is cut to butt against the shoulders formed by the overhanging jambs, after which regular door casing is applied to cover the joint and add a finished trim. Regular plasterboard nails are used to fasten the ½-in. sheets, spacing them 8 in. apart.

Where the plasterboard laps at an outside corner, the corner is reinforced with a strip of regular metal plaster beading. The nails that hold it, plus those holding the plasterboard, are later covered with joint compound.

Louvered bifold doors are ideal for shallow closets. They open wide for full access, help ventilate the closet and are good-looking. Two pairs of 15-in. doors will fit a 60-in. opening perfectly. They come complete with hardware and full instructions for hanging. Some even come ready-hinged and primed.

Completion of your closet requires adding matching baseboard along the floor and molding at the ceiling, and, of course, either papering or painting the walls if you used plasterboard.

Popular standards and brackets provide the easiest way to add shelves to your closet. Being fully adjustable, you can place the boards wherever you want them, and add as many as you want. Solid support is assured by locating the standards over studs. Where this can't be done, plastic screw anchors or fiber plugs should be used in plastered walls.

Use ½-in. plywood for the six shelves and support each one with five brackets. The trick in getting the 8-ft.-long shelves in place is to first put all six boards on the floor of the closet (resting them on edge) and then raise them one at a time as each of the five brackets is hooked in the standards. The brackets shown are of the heavy-duty type which features a plastic clip that's used for screwing the shelves to them.

PLASTERBOARD TREATMENT

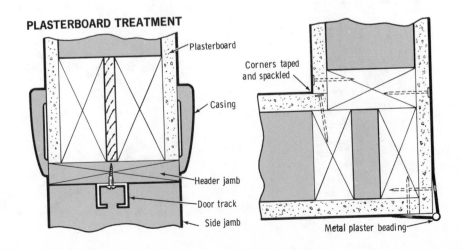

Plasterboard

Casing

Header jamb

Door track

Side jamb

Corners taped and spackled

Metal plaster beading

Make your closets work

■ IF YOU COMPILED a list of the 10 most common homeowner complaints, insufficient storage space, both for daily and seasonal use, would be sure to be high in the ratings. And, in most cases, the complaint is justified. Even new homes show a lack of thought in design and treatment of closet construction. However, since family needs vary, exactly how to get complete use of a closet depends upon what you need to store and for what length of time.

The bedroom closet, below, makes use of what previously was (and unfortunately in most homes is) wasted space. Built as shown in the sketch, the closet holds shirts, socks, and the like on handy sliding shelves. Extra shelves were installed above the clothes-hanger rod to handle seasonal items such as heavy clothing during the summer months.

BEDROOM CLOSET has hanger space reduced and pull-out shelves to meet the needs of the user.

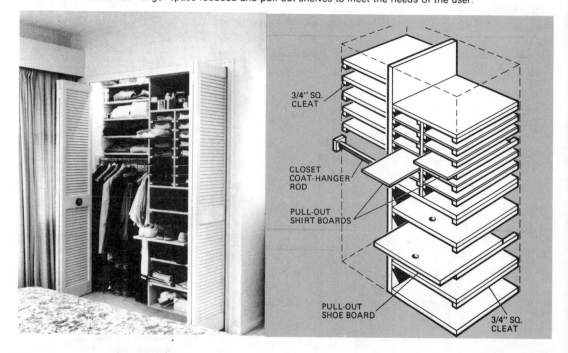

3/4″ SQ. CLEAT

CLOSET COAT-HANGER ROD

PULL-OUT SHIRT BOARDS

PULL-OUT SHOE BOARD

3/4″ SQ. CLEAT

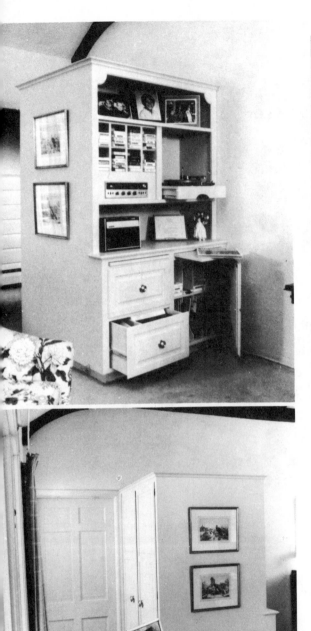

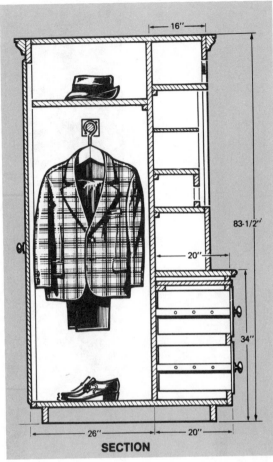

16"

83-1/2"

20"

34"

26"   20"

SECTION

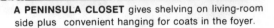

A PENINSULA CLOSET gives shelving on living-room side plus convenient hanging for coats in the foyer.

The second, and most elaborate "closet" is the peninsula unit which was added to the living room. The project initially started as a simple wall to shield living-room users from icy winter blasts each time the front door was opened. Because the living room could afford the floor space and the homeowners were imaginative planners, what would have been wasted space was used in a most practical way.

The front side of the unit faces the foyer and provides convenient hanging space for outerwear. The back side, facing the living room, has the look of a hutch. It houses stereo equipment, books and art objects, and also has pull-out counters for additional storage.

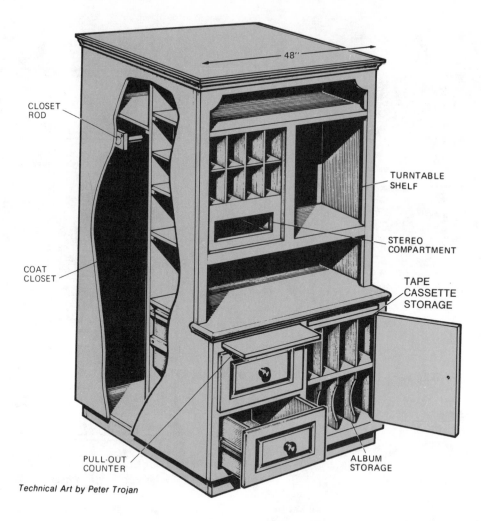

CLOSET ROD

TURNTABLE SHELF

STEREO COMPARTMENT

COAT CLOSET

TAPE CASSETTE STORAGE

48″

PULL-OUT COUNTER

ALBUM STORAGE

Technical Art by Peter Trojan

The third storage change made was to add a much-needed linen closet in the bath. Eight 15-in. open shelves are above the counter for towels and linens. Four cubes below are where two sons store boats and other kids' bathtub paraphernalia.

Other ideas you might consider: Even though they are 4 ft. or more wide, many closets in all rooms of the house have a single door for access. Why not install bypassing doors to permit easy access to the full closet?

Also, if it's structurally practical, don't overlook the possibility of using 8-ft.-high bifolds. These let you add shelves above that can make seasonal storage a snap. If you put the tall bifolds in bedrooms, each family member can then store his own clothing in one handy place instead of using the attic or basement. In this way everyone's clothing will be close at hand when it's needed.

A TOWEL CLOSET convenient to the sink has louvered bypassing doors to insure adequate circulation of air.

Computers: an introduction

■ NO INVENTION IN history has had the rapid, fundamental impact on humankind that the computer has. Over the past century, mass printing, the internal combustion engine, electricity and broadcasting have radically changed the ways in which we live and work. But in less than 50 years the computer has forever changed the basic ways in which we organize information, solve problems and create new approaches. The results are so profound that they are hard to grasp.

The computer has been called the "mind appliance" because it helps us think in larger, more orderly patterns. It does this by expanding the quantity and quality of complex information we need to make sensible "brain-based" decisions about economics, ecology, society, science and technology. The computer releases our intellects like the space capsule has released our bodies. It takes us beyond traditional limits.

A brief history

The computer did not spring, fully formed, onto the stage of history. Instead, it resulted from several centuries of disappointing efforts to make a reliable calculating machine. Most of these projects involved complicated arrangements of gears, wheels and springs. Some of the devices actually worked—but slowly at best. The familiar adding machine of recent vintage was the culmination of the effort.

The birth of the electronic tube—the heart of broadcasting—around the second decade of the century gave some scientists an idea: Why couldn't they substitute a variety of these fast, new "on/off" contrivances for the counting ratchets of the mechanical calculators?

The ABC of computers. Nobody really made much progress until a young mathematician named John V. Atanasoff at Iowa State University came up with a basic design. That was in late 1937. With the help of a graduate student named Clifford Berry, Professor Atanasoff built the first electronic, digital computer, which he called the ABC (Atanasoff-Berry-Computer). But its existence was virtually unknown outside a very narrow academic circle.

ENGLISHMAN CHARLES BABBAGE was first to realize with this Difference Engine that a machine could remember numbers, do simple arithmetic and be programmed to calculate automatically. His later Analytic Engine would have been the first computer if mechanical engineers in the early 1800s could have built one from his designs.

THE GIANT ENIAC computer of 1946 weighed 30 tons, contained 18,000 vacuum tubes and filled several rooms.

Enter ENIAC. During the early days of World War II, the ABC attracted the attention of a mathematician from Pennsylvania named Dr. John Mauchly. He had been asked by the U.S. Army to find a faster way of computing artillery trajectories. With the assistance of another graduate student named Presper Eckert, Dr. Mauchly succeeded in building a much larger electronic computer dubbed ENIAC (Electronic Numerical Integrator and Computer). That 30-ton monster, made up of 18,000 heat-producing vacuum tubes, was put into service right after the war ended. It enormously reduced the time required to do repetitive calculations. The ensuing publicity ushered in the Age of the Computer—this in spite of the fact that ENIAC went dark every few hours because of the unreliable nature of the many vacuum tubes required.

While ABC and ENIAC were true computers, they lacked the versatility of their descendants. Both could be programmed only by having their circuits rewired, a painstaking process at best.

Programs and programming. The solution to this drawback came from another mathematician named John von Neumann. He showed how the computer's program (its recipe for doing the desired calculations) could actually be stored in the computer itself as an electrical memory just as

the data (numbers) to be processed were. This meant that new programs could be developed and entered far more easily.

Hollerith cards. All early computers were designed to have data entered in the form of paper tapes or punch cards. The sophisticated mechanical technologies for doing this had been developed around the turn of the century by Herman Hollerith. The corporation that manufactured most of the machines was IBM, destined to become the world giant of computing.

A commercial venture—the UNIVAC. Another corporate giant was Remington-Rand, the first real computer manufacturer. It was for that farsighted firm that Mauchly and Eckert designed the first commercially available computer, the famous UNIVAC I. The first buyer was the U.S. Census Bureau. The year was 1951.

Hardware and software developments. For two decades thereafter, the progress of computing was rather undramatic. The machines of the period were large, extremely expensive and relatively awkward to use. For most people they were out of sight and out of mind. But important developments were taking place all the same.

On the hardware side, the invention of the miniature transistor, a replacement for the vacuum tube, reduced both size and cost. A subsequent shift to the integrated chip—each of which had thousands of transistor circuits printed on a tiny ceramic surface far smaller than the original transistors themselves—vastly accelerated this downward spiral. Related discoveries in telecommunications made it possible for computers to share information—with each other as well as with thousands of individual users.

On the software side, talented specialists like Commodore Grace Hopper of the U.S. Navy, John Backus of IBM and Dr. John Kameny of Dartmouth moved to install high-level computer languages such as FORTRAN, COBOL and BASIC. These improved programming procedures permitted ordinary people to use computers to do many more tasks—and far more quickly. No longer were the machines used only as mammoth counters and calculators. They became storage files for mind-boggling numbers of facts. Moreover, they could process the data into new, useful forms while analyzing them to discover sophisticated relationships and patterns.

The microcomputer emerges. The stage was set for the quantum leap needed to make computing a pervasive human capability. The event was the development in 1969 of the microprocessor on a tiny inexpensive silicon chip. The individual responsible was Dr. Ted Hoff, an engineer at Intel Corporation in California. In an attempt to make a better desk-top calculator, Dr. Hoff conceived the innovative idea of placing all the arithmetic and logic circuits on a single integrated chip. This meant that the central functions of a full-fledged

A TYPICAL MICROPROCESSOR CHIP contains thousands of circuits, resistors, capacitors and transistors.

THE APPLE I COMPUTER built in Steve Wozniak's garage in 1976. Acceptance of this first attempt by Jobs and Wozniak led them to form Apple Inc., the first giant of the microcomputer industry.

computer could be contained on a ceramic device not much larger than a fingernail!

In 1975, an unpretentious article in a hobbyist magazine described the technique for building a sure-enough computer around the new microprocessors that were then blossoming on the market. The article was based on an actual kit sold by a small electronics firm called MITS in Albuquerque, New Mexico. The design was largely the creation of an enterprising electrical engineer named H. Edward Roberts. The ALTAIR 8800, as the kit machine was called, was the world's first real digital microcomputer.

In 1976, two talented young men in California, Steve Jobs and Steve Wozniak, designed and put together their own microcomputer. They tried to sell it to Wozniak's employer, Hewlett-Packard, but had no luck. Then they demonstrated it to their fellow members of the Homebrew Computer Club. There it was a decided hit. Word began to spread in the community. A local computer store actually ordered 50 of the little wonders—engagingly dubbed the Apple by its delighted developers. The Wozniak garage was the first assembly line for the world's first ready-made home computer.

The almost bewildering success of the Apple gave rise to a whole new microcomputer industry. Brand names like Commodore, Atari, Sinclair and TRS-80 became household words. Products bearing them were available not only in a rash of slick new computer stores located in great suburban shopping centers but also at humble general stores in remote rural villages all across the country. In 1981 some 300,000 micros were sold to the public. One year later the number skyrocketed to over 3 million. The

THE APPLE II was the first microcomputer to make it big on the open market in the late 1970s and early 1980s.

growth has slowed only a bit. And the direction is still clearly upward. Having multiple computers in virtually every home, office, school, business and farm seems altogether likely within a decade or so.

The mind appliance. The reason for the success of the microcomputer is not hard to understand. It's found in the phrase "mind appliance," coined by distinguished MIT professor Dr. Seymour Papert. Various home appliances like toasters, dishwashers and vacuum cleaners caught on quickly over the years because they permitted us to "do more with less effort." So does the microcomputer. It allows us to do word processing, number crunching, data manipulation and graphing in the twinkling of an eye. It also helps us learn new skills and facts more quickly and with less tedium.

On top of all those valuable functions, it lets us play vividly exciting games. Yet for many users, computing is great fun in itself, even without the arcade games. It has opened up new and constructive ways of dealing with the world around us.

Computing has begun to transform the intellectual—and workaday—landscape for each of us, and in fewer than 50 years. Quite an achievement for such a deceptively simple device.

What is a computer?

A computer is an electronic device for rapidly processing many numbers. That may not seem an adequate definition, since so many of the marvelous tasks a computer accomplishes have to do with words and graphics rather than numbers.

The computer treats all letters, punctuation marks, graphic effects and other input as binary numbers. The binary system (Base 2) uses only zeroes and ones to represent any number in our more familiar Base 10 decimal system. For example, the binary number "11111111" is really 256 in our everyday decimal number system.

The binary system is useful to the computer for the simple reason that its two digits (1,0) can be electronically treated as "on/off ." A computer circuit can count binary numbers by being turned "on" or "off" to correspond to the binary number being processed. The binary number "101" [decimal 5] would pass through the computer's internal circuits as "on-off-on."

This characteristic wouldn't mean much if the computer circuitry took a long time to operate its "ons" and "offs." But the fact is that the integrated chip used as the computer's CPU (central processing unit) does its work at almost instantaneous rates.

Bits and Bytes. Fundamentally, all computing is based on the processing of binary numbers in a highly organized way. Each atom of information—that is, each "on" or "off"—is called a "bit" (**bi**nary dig**it**). These bits are arranged into larger units called "bytes." The size of each byte varies with the kind of computer involved. The two most common sizes are 8-bit and 16-bit, although 32-bit machines may soon become routine in certain applications. (There are also some pocket computers in which the bits are grouped into 4-unit half-bytes, appropriately called "nibbles.")

A single binary number is always encoded within one or more of these byte structures. In the instance of the binary number "101," the full byte statement in an 8-bit computer would be "00000101," or off-off-off-off-off-on-off-on.

Logic gates. The basic processing unit of any computer is a "logic gate." Many millions of such minuscule units are found in all upscale computers. A logic gate is an electronic arrangement by which low-voltage electricity is switched through parallel circuits. The computer program determines which logic gates are used as a step in the overall process.

The logic gates compare numbers (in the form of voltages) in various ways to see if they are similar or different. Depending on the particular program being used in the computer, the answers are then fed along to subsequent logic gates until it gets the desired result.

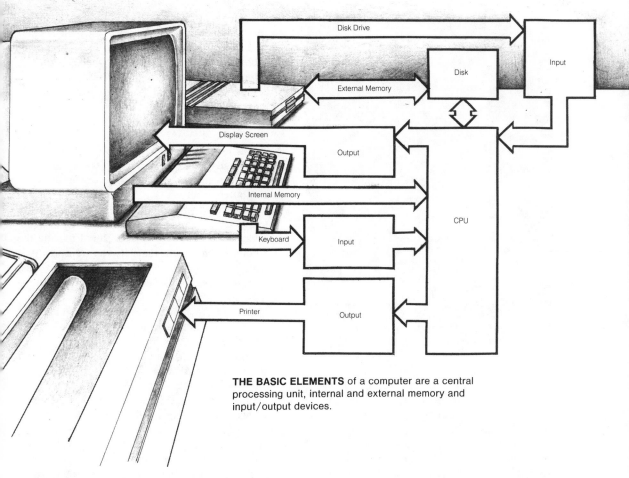

THE BASIC ELEMENTS of a computer are a central processing unit, internal and external memory and input/output devices.

Suppose, for example, you had filed the telephone number "1-800-247-5470" in your micro's data-base program. Now, months later, you want to recall to whom it belongs. You input the number. The computer has been programmed to check through the telephone file to locate that particular sequence. In a second or so, the computer's internal logic gates will have compared hundreds, even hundreds of thousands, of numbers to match the correct one—all by sending voltage "ons" and "offs" through appropriate logic gates!

The architecture of a computer

Computer systems, both large and small, have three elements: a CPU (central processing unit), memory and I/O (input/output).

The Central Processing Unit (CPU). In a microcomputer, the CPU is apt to be a single integrated chip containing the equivalent of thousands of transistors or tubes. The CPU's functions are, broadly, twofold: It controls the sequence and direction of all operations, and it governs the arithmetic and logic procedures used in any processing. The CPU manages the computer.

There are many different kinds of CPUs on the market. The principal manufacturers include Intel, Zilog, Motorola, CMOS and Texas Instruments. Each model is distinctive in its operating characteristics. The most frequently applied labels have to do with their internal byte structures. At one time, 8-bit CPUs dominated the scene. Now they share the market with 16-bit and 32-bit variations.

While the bit count of a CPU is important, that figure by itself cannot tell you much about the speed, capacity and reliability of the computer that depends on it. There are many other important factors of computer design that affect performance.

Internal memory. Memory in a computer is a series of electronic storage points. Both program instructions and data are kept in memory at various times. There are two kinds of internal memory. Both come in the form of silicon chips.

Read-only-memory (ROM) has certain operating instructions "burned in" at the factory. These

TYPICAL OF HOME MICROCOMPUTERS in the mid-1980s, this Commodore 128 has more processing capacity than the giant ENIAC did just 4 decades ago.

can't be erased (although they can be damaged). The CPU relies on these ROM instructions to carry out many housekeeping tasks, such as finding the circuit addresses of keys and printers.

The ROM is the part of the computer in which its deepest "personality traits" are stored—the special ways in which the computer (mainly the CPU) reacts to input. The correct term for this important aspect of the computer's architecture is "operating system."

There are many different kinds of DOS: AppleDos, PC-DOS, MS-DOS, TRS-DOS, CP/M, etc. Most of them are designed to run a particular brand or model of computer. Some of them, like the well-known CP/M, have been translated into a number of machine-specific subversions in order to run a variety of different brands and models.

Others of them, however, can be used directly by a number of different machines that are technically compatible with each other. The best examples of this are the several dozen different micros that are so-called "IBM-compatible." All of these look-alikes will run on PC-DOS, the IBM disk operating system. (And to complicate things a bit, they will also run on MS-DOS, the original proprietary DOS on which PC-DOS was closely based.)

Most commercial software programs are designed to operate within specified DOS command structures.

Random-access-memory (RAM) is available for the temporary storage of data or particular programs (always kept in the form of binary numbers). It is RAM that people are usually talking about when they characterize a given computer model as having so many bytes of memory. Nowadays home computers range from 16K up to about 512K RAM. Office micros are more apt to have 128K to 640K RAM. (The "K" stands for kilobytes—1,024 to be exact. In everyday language, it means simply 1,000 bytes.)

External memory. All the memory needed by a computer is not actually built into its own internal circuitry. That would be too expensive and too inconvenient. Often you want a way of keeping massive amounts of data stored outside the computer, in a form that lets you transport it at will. That's why manufacturers developed such storage media as paper cards and tapes along with magnetic tapes and disks.

Each of these media has the ability to keep binary coding generated by the computer in large quantities.

Microcomputers rarely make use of the paper storage forms because of the specialized equipment needed to process them. Instead, they use magnetic media like cassette tapes, floppy diskettes and hard disks. All of these forms depend on electricity to leave a track of magnetic "ons/offs" that can be read back into the computer as binary information.

Tape storage. The cassette tapes are sequential (i.e., linear) storage devices. They cannot be used where data access rates must be rapid. The disk formats, in various sizes and electronic configurations, permit extremely quick random accessing of the stored data materials. Therefore, they are most frequently found in high-pressure business applications. This is especially true of the fix-mounted hard disk, which has a much greater storage capacity than removable floppy diskettes. It also costs a great deal more.

Disk storage. The floppy forms come in several sizes, ranging from 8-in. down to around 3-in. The most common size, however, is 5¼ in. All of these media consist of a nonrigid plastic disk coated with a magnetic film like that used on regular audio tapes. The disk is encased in a hard plastic envelope that has a circular opening cut to permit a centered hole in the disk itself to be affixed to a rotating drive shaft. A second opening along a single quadrant of the envelope allows the laterally moving disk head structure to make rapid physical contact with the spinning surface in order to read or write data codes on magnetically embedded circular tracks.

HE MOST COMMON FORM of external memory
orage is a floppy diskette like this 5¼-in. type.

Some floppy disks can record on both sides, others only on one. Some have two to four times the storage density of others. (And certain exotic models increase the ratio to several times 4!) All diskettes require some sort of guide marker hole to help position the rapidly moving head to find the correct data track. Soft-sectored models use but a single such marker hole; hard-sectored versions require a sequence of several. These marker holes are customarily placed near the center rim and are accessible by the disk drive mechanism through one or more holes cut in the hard plastic envelope.

Before any disk can be used by a computer to store data, it must be put through a short process called "formating." Each kind of DOS has its own formating procedures. In all cases, the principle is the same. The DOS directs the magnetic drive head to lay down on the raw surface of the

A FLOPPY DISKETTE contains a round disc with a magnetic surface, a recording window so the head can reach the disc, a large hole or hub for the drive spindle, one or more locating holes for drive indexing, all enclosed in a vinyl protective jacket with a friction-free liner.

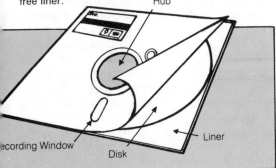

Hub

Liner

ecording Window

Disk

disk a specific pattern of circular tracks and sectors into which data can be loaded, and from which it can then later be retrieved.

Disk formats are not interchangeable. For example, a disk formated for an IBM microcomputer system cannot be read or written to by an Apple disk drive, or vice versa. (There are several software programs on the market, however, that do permit helpful translations to occur between certain different disk formats.)

Diskettes cost from one to five dollars each, depending on size, version, density and quality. Cassette tapes of computer quality run in the same cost range for lengths of from 10 to 20 minutes.

Input/output devices. The I/O elements of an average computer can be tremendously varied. They can include such components and peripherals as keyboards, display screens, printers, modems (used to link computers through telephone lines), touch-pads, light pens and joysticks—even interactive videodiscs. All have one thing in common. They are instruments that can help you enter data—or, conversely, witness its subsequent output. (The term "peripheral" is sometimes applied to equipment that is not absolutely necessary to the practical operation of the CPU. Essential gear is often called a "component").

Printers. For many users, a printer is an absolutely necessary computer component. This is certainly true for the many people who use their micros as word processors. Printers constitute a rather complicated technical clan. They come in many varieties, and with a very broad cost range to match.

Dot matrix. The simplest and least expensive printers are called dot matrix types. They form their letters and other characters through the use of a special head device consisting of a small rectangular matrix of tiny mechanized styluses. Various dotted patterns of the styluses can be momentarily projected forward against a passing inked ribbon. The ribbon is thus forced into contact with the surface of a sheet of paper that has been inserted into the printer platen roller. It leaves its mark in the form of a printed character bearing a reverse of the styluses' pattern. The dot patterns of the styluses represent letters, numbers, punctuation marks and graphics characters.

The matrixed head is mounted on a slider that moves laterally across the paper. At the right margin point, geared mechanisms are usually programmed to turn the paper roller forward one or more rows and to return the head to the start of the left-most column.

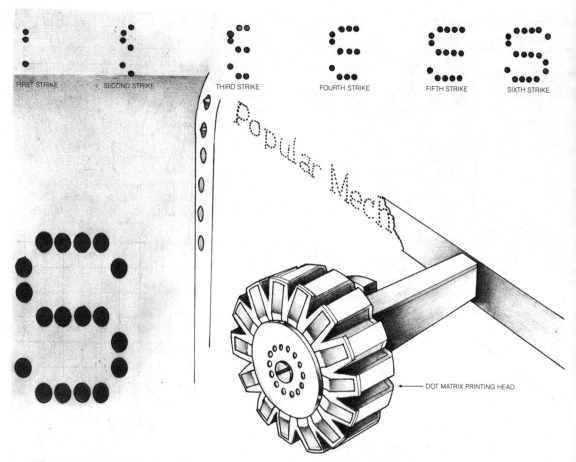

FIRST STRIKE   SECOND STRIKE   THIRD STRIKE   FOURTH STRIKE   FIFTH STRIKE   SIXTH STRIKE

DOT MATRIX PRINTING HEAD

A DOT MATRIX PRINTER uses a series of wires that strike the paper through a ribbon, creating dots in a pattern to form letters, numbers and symbols.

Certain printing effects are gained from the dot matrix printer by having the head mechanism go back over lines, adding new characters (like an underline) or simply restriking over existing ones in order to darken their appearance.

Dot matrix printers themselves range from the fairly primitive to virtual letter quality. The term "letter quality" means simply that the printed materials in question look as if they had actually been typewritten on a high-quality electric machine.

The most primitive dot matrix printers have fewer dots per character (and clearly show it). They often do not have what are called "true descenders." This jargon means that letters that usually have parts that descend below the line (like q,y,p,g, and j) are all printed above the line. This makes them look quite odd. And ugly. These simpler printers, sometimes referred to as "draft quality," are used largely to print out list-

ings of computer program codes or other such workaday "stuff."

Daisy wheels. The other important category of computer printer is called daisy wheel type. These are inevitably letter quality, because they are all typewriters in disguise. Some, in fact, really are electric typewriters that have an interface with a controlling computer.

A daisy wheel is a plastic device about 3 in. in diameter. The daisy is composed of typebars or "petals" with a letter, number or symbol at the tip of each. A special rotating mechanism whirls the mounted daisy wheel around from character to character, much like the more familiar ball used on many electric typewriters. (The ball formation sometimes replaces the daisy wheel in computer printers.)

One nice thing about a daisy wheel printer is the fact that you can buy a variety of different fonts (typefaces) and easily change them around.

The bad thing about them is that nearly all of them are much slower than dot matrix types. The less you pay, the slower they go.

Even though a particular printer can link to a particular computer in one of only two ways, the actual fitting together can sometimes be an arduous task. Finding the exact connecting cable, setting the printer's tiny dip switches, modifying software output commands and establishing control codes can take hours of hard work. You are usually well advised to let a competent computer store figure out the hooking up for you before you take the new printer home or to the office.

As to cost, all the way from $200 to $2,000! Or more!

The home micro system. The buyer of a typical microcomputer package generally receives the CPU (placed inside a console unit), a keyboard, an external memory storage device (like a disk drive) and a cathode ray tube (CRT) screen or video monitor. Printers and other peripheral devices generally must be bought separately from the basic system. (Home computers often make use of a regular TV set for screen output rather

A TYPICAL MICROCOMPUTER WORKSTATION in a home used for word processing, budgeting, telecommunications—and games.

THE DAISY WHEEL'S "petals" contain the numbers and characters that are pressed against the ribbon and paper, as the wheel spins to the proper position.

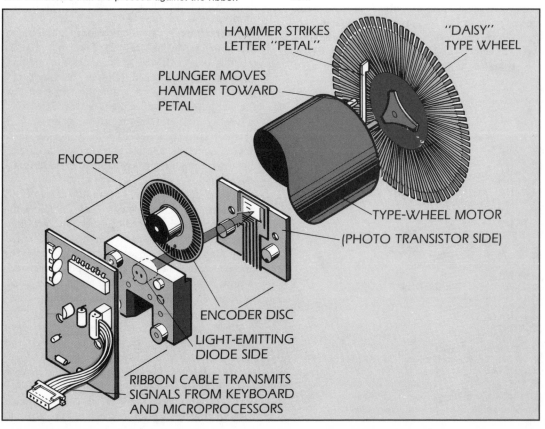

HAMMER STRIKES LETTER "PETAL"

"DAISY" TYPE WHEEL

PLUNGER MOVES HAMMER TOWARD PETAL

ENCODER

TYPE-WHEEL MOTOR

(PHOTO TRANSISTOR SIDE)

ENCODER DISC

LIGHT-EMITTING DIODE SIDE

RIBBON CABLE TRANSMITS SIGNALS FROM KEYBOARD AND MICROPROCESSORS

than requiring a separate CRT or video monitor. These same computers usually use cassette storage rather than disk.)

Computer languages

It has been noted that computers can become more versatile through the use of "high-level" languages. This is because such computer languages allow the user or programmer to develop task processes much more quickly and easily than if binary numbers are directly used for the purpose of telling the machine what to do and when to do it.

Since the 1950s, people have been busy developing hundreds of these special languages. Some were almost as difficult as the binary coding they were intended to replace. Many others focused entirely on single computing tasks, such as monitoring weather statistics. But a few proved a real boon to computer users.

For the microcomputerist, the list is not a long one at all:

BASIC (Beginners All-Purpose Symbolic Instruction Code)—a language developed by Professors Kameny and Kurtz at Dartmouth College to enable their students to get into computing quickly. It makes use of English words and organizes the program into discrete, numbered steps. Virtually every microcomputer on the market comes equipped with a BASIC interpreter. It is the most widely used of all computer languages. Unfortunately, it has been divided into a number of dialects that are not mutually understood by all micros.

PASCAL (named for the famous French mathematician)—a sophisticated language not unlike BASIC except that its programming structure is more logical and orderly. Tasks are executed in neatly structured sequences that are easier to "debug"—correct—than BASIC.

FORTRAN (FORmula TRANslating System)—a language developed by John Backus and others at IBM for special uses in the scientific community. It has many characteristics in common with BASIC, which was based on it. English words and mathematical statements predominate.

COBOL (COmmon Business-Oriented Language)—a variant of the FORTRAN model designed to make business computing easier in such task areas as mailing lists, billing and accounting. It was the first language specifically designed to move between different brands and models of computers. It has little following outside the commercial sector.

ASSEMBLY—a somewhat lower-level language that sends abbreviated word-code instructions to the computer through a special software form called an assembler. It makes heavy use of hexadecimal numbers in place of the binary numbers of machine language. Hexadecimal numbers (Base 16) are a bit easier to handle than their binary cousins (Base 2). The chief characteristics of ASSEMBLY language are its tiny steps and its high speed. (One of the drawbacks of high-level languages is that they tend to slow the computer down on some tasks.) ASSEMBLY is heavily used in designing arcade games.

Other languages like PL/1, Forth and ADA have important applications in special areas. They are not generally available to the microprocessor field.

Many—perhaps most—computer users do no programming of their own. They operate software programs developed by others. It is a widely held view in the computer industry that programming skills are becoming less necessary to the serious user because so much varied software is now available on the open market. You don't need to do much of your own designing nowadays.

Word processing. One of the earlier achievements was the design of programs to permit the computer to perform word processing. A typist entered the text through a teletypewriter keyboard as usual, but with the "magical" ability to make instant corrections on a video monitor without erasing. A printer turned out the finished paper copies in record time. The technique made

```
ST
100 PRINT
110 PRINT "POPULAR MECHANICS METRIC"
120 PRINT "    CONVERSION PROGRAM"
130 PRINT
140 PRINT "A-INCHES TO CENTIMETERS"
150 PRINT "B-POUNDS TO KILOGRAMS"
160 PRINT "X-END PROGRAM"
170 PRINT
180 INPUT "ENTER YOUR SELECTION";S$
190 IF S$ = "A" THEN GOTO220
200 IF S$ = "B" THEN GOTO270
210 IF S$<>"A" OR S$<>"B" THEN GOTO320
220 PRINT
230 INPUT "ENTER LENGTH IN INCHES";I
240 LET C = 2.54*I
250 PRINT I;"INCHES IS = TO";C;"CENTIMETERS"
260 GOTO100
270 PRINT
280 INPUT "INPUT WEIGHT IN POUNDS";P
290 LET K = .4536*P
300 PRINT P;"POUNDS IS = TO";K;"KILOGRAMS"
310 GOTO100
320 END
```

A LISTING of part of a computer program written in the popular BASIC language developed in 1964 at Dartmouth College by Kameny and Kurtz.

a noticeable difference over traditional typing procedures when it came time to make cut-and-paste corrections and spin off multiple textual variations. A few deft keystrokes and the job was completed—almost automatically.

Data processing. Another early computer application was called data processing. It involved making, filing and sorting complex business records. The initial processes closely paralleled the mechanical card systems that IBM and others had developed before the electronic digital computer even appeared on the market.

Microcomputer users see great value in data-processing applications, even though they are usually much simpler than those of corporate business or the scientific laboratory. Financial record keeping for tax preparation has become a high priority for family-based computers. Hobbyists delight in the ease with which inexpensive data-base programs can keep collection inventories of their records, books or stamps to a near professional accuracy.

Spreadsheets. One of the most imaginative applications of a microcomputer is found in the so-called "electronic spreadsheet" programs such as VISI-CALC. These software packages allow you to set up a wide range of "what if?" mathematical models. Typing in a few figures can quickly yield a series of computed consequences. For example, you can enter varying interest rates to see what effects they would have on your mortgage, savings account or budget plans.

The newer of these remarkable spreadsheet applications, such as the popular Lotus 1-2-3, have been cunningly integrated with ingenious graphing programs. By touching a few keys, spreadsheet results can be illustrated on screen or printer with high-quality charts and graphs done in appealing colors.

Other software. The range of software available for computers has become almost as wide as the categories of books in a well-stocked library. Not only are there word-processing, data-processing, spreadsheet and graphing programs, there are games, psychological tests and interactive lessons on almost any academic topic imaginable. Costs range from about $10 for simple games to several hundred dollars for sophisticated spreadsheets or word-processing programs.

Much of the software must be acquired from a computer store. But there are other means of acquisition as well. Many people subscribe to special data sources like Compuserve and The Source. By dialing up a special telephone number through an inexpensive device called a modem attached to your computer, you can access a

WORD PROCESSING is the most widely used application of the microcomputer in offices and homes.

massive mainframe computer laden with fascinating data-bases and software programs. These can then be "down-loaded" into your own computer. Fees are modest.

Local computer clubs often run smaller data-base services called bulletin boards. These, too, are accessed through modems and telephone calls, but usually without subscription fees of any consequence.

The clubs will frequently allow callers to copy software programs designed by their own members (nicknamed "hackers"). The scope of their content is very broad: games, word processing, data matrices, instruction—you name it! Sometimes these homemade efforts are quite amateurish, but more often they are of a very high quality. Good programmers seem to abound these days. This sort of "public domain" software is of increasing importance in many personal software libraries. Here is additional proof of the strong impact computers are having on us. We are fast becoming a nation of active computerists.

Computer monitors

■ IF YOU'RE USING your computer hooked up to the family TV set, you've already discovered this arrangement is far from ideal. Not only does it upset family TV viewing habits but it gives you less-than-ideal screen display of text, graphics and games from your computer. A TV set is designed to pull in programs off the airwaves, not for high-precision computer display.

Types of display devices

There are three basic types of display devices for computers in use today, with promise of technology breakthroughs for other types of displays in the near future. The output from your computer can be displayed on a standard television receiver, a composite video monitor, or an RGB display screen. The type of display device you can use with your computer depends on the internal circuits of the computer itself. So before you run out to buy the very best, be sure your computer has the circuitry to drive it.

Factors affecting screen display

A gun in a cathode ray tube fires a beam of electrons at a phosphor on the face of the tube as the beam moves left to right, top to bottom forming ideal-size fields of 262½ lines interlaced in pairs for 525-line frames—each frame repeated 30 times a second.

In a color tube, there are clusters of red, green and blue dots, bars or stripes etched on the face. The size of these triads obviously limits the number of lines the electron can scan to form each image. The result is a sacrifice in picture sharpness or resolution. Monochrome screens, with a continuous phosphor coating, do not share this problem.

The intensity of the picture at any one point depends on how strong the electron beam is at that given point. Color depends also on where the beam is aimed. This is analog control, varying the intensity and aim of the electron beam to form the picture.

Most computers, on the other hand, generate on/off digital information. Instead of varying the intensity of a continuous sweep of the electron beam, the computer looks at the scanning of the tube as a series of dots or pixels to turn on or off depending on the display desired. Each row of dots is "written" by the electron beam as it scans across the tube.

Computers form letters or numbers on the screen in a matrix of dots or pixels, most in a 63-dot matrix that is 7 dots wide by 9 dots high. This can range from as coarse as a 35-dot matrix (5 by 7) to a high resolution matrix of more than 300 dots. When you allow for blank rows of dots between lines of characters, it can take 10 to 12 scanning lines to draw a row of characters. Patterns of these dots or pixels are turned on for graphic displays.

Clarity or sharpness of the picture on the screen can be thought of in terms of how many vertical lines of these dots can be seen across the tube and how many horizontal lines of dots can be seen down the face of the screen.

Horizontal resolution, determined by the bandwidth of a display device, tells how many vertical lines across the screen can be displayed. Bandwidth is a measure of how fast information can be written to the screen. The faster a complete screen of information can be written, the more vertical lines will be seen. Bandwidth is expressed in how many millions of times the screen is written each second (MHz). To display a screen with 25 rows of 80 characters (each character in a 7 by 9 matrix), a video display device must have a 9 MHz bandwidth. A 40-column display would require only half the speed—4.5 MHz.

Vertical resolution tells how many horizontal

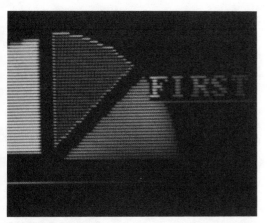 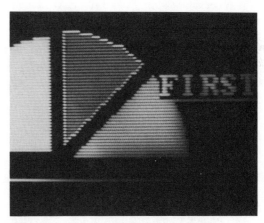

SCREENS OF A high-res color monitor (left) and a low-res monitor (right) show the difference in resolution. The high-res monitor has a greater bandwidth; the picture of the low-res monitor appears out of focus because of the lower resolution of each individual color dot.

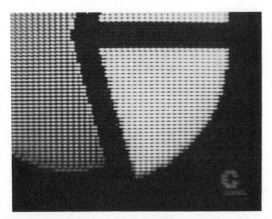 

IN A MONOCHROME monitor, each scanning line on the screen contains a series of locations (pixels) which are illuminated to form a graphic picture or character. Note in the closeup (right) that each pixel is approximately twice as wide as it is high.

lines down the face of the tube the device will display. In practice, the standard 525-line screen will have a vertical resolution of only 343 lines. You probably are seeing only about 260 lines of resolution on your TV set when you watch the nightly evening news. This is okay for family TV entertainment viewing but not so good for the display of text from a computer's word processing program.

Dot size is another factor affecting sharpness. When the electron beam hits the phosphor on the face of the tube, other electrons are forced off the layer of phosphor, hit the face of the tube and bounce back. This creates a "halo" around the dot. When these halos get too big, or halos on adjacent lines overlap, the picture loses sharpness. The smaller the spot turned on by the electron beam, the sharper the picture. The dot size of a TV set can be as much as 0.10mm. On a high resolution color monitor it can be half that—0.05mm—which is one reason why monitors generally give sharper, clearer pictures.

TV receivers

When television pictures are broadcast, the signal controlling the electron beam is wrapped in an envelope called a radio frequency carrier wave (RF signal). There's a different envelope frequency for each TV channel. The tuner in your receiver strips away the carrier wave envelope for the channel you select leaving only the composite of the video signal for each color to be sent to the picture tube.

The amount of information for both the video signals and the carrier waves must be contained within a limited band of frequencies for broadcast. The broadcast of these signals requires receivers to have greater tolerances, and a lot of unwanted signals and noise are picked up along the way. Generally, the greater the bandwidth of your TV set, the greater will be the sharpness or resolution of the picture. But, you can't expect to see more than what's left after the tuner strips away the RF signals.

Computers that allow you to use a television receiver as the video display terminal have a built-in modulator that combines the 3 color signals and other information then wraps the composite signal in an envelope for either Channel 3 or Channel 4 (usually switchable) where it is sent by wire to the antenna terminals on your TV set to be unwrapped by the tuner, decoded and displayed.

With a color TV set, resolution of a computer image is seldom more than 16 rows of 40 characters each.

Composite video monitors

A monitor is designed to display the video signals from a computer, VCR or camera with a higher resolution and without the complicating and limiting circuits used to unwrap the RF carrier frequency from the picture information. Because monitors don't have to leave tolerances for the tuner to translate broadcast signals, they can be made to much closer specifications resulting in higher resolution. Connections to a monitor go directly to the video amplifiers, bypassing the antenna terminals and tuner circuits.

They are called *composite* video monitors because the red, green and blue signals are combined with other information the tube needs to be sent over a single wire bypassing any tuner circuits in the device then split apart to be sent to the appropriate place on the screen for a color display.

Almost always substituting a monitor for a TV set (if your computer has a composite video output) will mean a noticeable increase in picture sharpness and often an increase in the number of lines that can be displayed. Monochrome monitors can give you a readable screen of at least 25 rows of 80 characters each, while some color displays of text may still be limited to 40 characters in less expensive color monitors because of the limited bandwidth or resolution. Graphic displays on monochrome monitors can display 320 rows of 640 dots each—or more in some specialized graphic terminals.

RGB displays

With an RGB display screen, each of the three primary signals—red, green and blue—and the luminance signal controlling brightness—are sent out of the computer from different circuits over separate wires. These connections are made with a multiple-pin connector from your computer. The signals are never combined into a composite signal in the computer so they never have to be separated in the monitor. Each enters its own circuit to fire an electron gun when it scans the tube in the exact location of that color dot. The result is greatly increased sharpness of the picture. Because of the preciseness of these circuits, manufacturers of RGB displays such as Taxan can give you a color picture that is 400 lines of pixels, 720 across—but at a premium cost.

The RGB circuits in the computer can deliver a digital signal for each of the colors. These displays are restricted to the 8 colors that can be made from the red, blue and green phosphor dots lit in combination at the same intensity. Some

RGB display circuits deliver analog information to the tube. The result is almost unlimited variations in the colors and brightness levels. Most offer "pallets" of 512 colors, but the potential is much greater. Your computer must be able to send each of the 3 color signals separately or you cannot use an RGB monitor. The type of connections available between the computer and the monitor can usually tell you if it can.

What to look for

The factors you should look for in a display unit for your computer are computer capacity, bandwidth, dot pitch, screen size, color, accessories and cost.

Computer capacity will determine the kind of display device you should invest in. Adding a high resolution Taxan Model 440 monitor will do little good with an Atari computer that only sends out 191 lines of information. A high-res color RGB is a waste of money with the Sanyo MBC-1250 computer which has the high-res graphics, but no circuits to drive a color signal. In a similar manner, your picture sharpness is not going to be great by adding the 80-column board to a Commodore 64 if the color monitor you're using has a bandwidth limiting the display to 40 characters.

Bandwidth determines the sharpness or resolution of the picture displayed. It is usually measured in millions of cycles per second (MHz). As a rule of thumb, you can expect about 80 lines of horizontal resolution from each MHz of bandwidth. TV sets typically have a bandwidth of 3.8 to 4.5 MHz; a good monitor can have a bandwidth of 50 MHz. Most manufacturers of computer monitors and RGB displays specify bandwidth as lines of resolution while TV sets are more likely to express this in MHz, if at all.

Dot pitch is the size of each red, green and blue dot and the space between them. A color display is limited to the number of triads of red, green and blue dots, bars or stripes etched on the face of the tube. Monochrome screens, with a single continuous phosphor, can have a much smaller dot pitch and higher resolution. High resolution color monitors can have a dot pitch of 0.05mm but a color TV set can be twice that. Manufacturers of computer monitors often express dot pitch in terms of the matrix of dots or pixels on the entire screen. Typical specs range from the 320 by 200 pixels of the Commodore C-1702 monitor to the 720 by 420 pixels of Amdek's Color IV RGB display.

Screen size does not follow the rule that more is better. The best screen size for a monitor for close-in work is 12 inches diagonal measure whether it's monochrome or color. This is because most computing is done with your eyes approximately 18 to 20 inches from the screen. If you plan to use the monitor for a lot of game play, then 13 inches is an ideal size. The extra inch *does* make a difference. As screen size gets too small, however, the "halos" of the dots overlap producing a fuzzy picture.

Color depends on what you use your computer for. If you do a lot of business-type work, you're much better off getting a monochrome display which typically has much higher resolution. If you also plan to do color bar charts or play some computer games you need a color monitor. You might want to get both kinds of monitors and connect them to the computer using a selector switch, an inexpensive item available in most computer stores.

Monochrome displays are not called black and white screen any more. A screen with a green phosphor (green letters on a black background) is now almost the monochrome standard in the U.S. Amber screens are gaining in popularity because they're very legible and cause less eyestrain. They are about the only kind you can buy in Europe.

Accessories. Some monitors are really bare bones when it comes to controls. Some have two knobs on the front labeled PULL-ON and BRIGHT. Others have enough control knobs to operate a Space Shuttle. The brightness and contrast of the image on the screen can affect the

FLAT SCREEN is a sandwich of microcomponents.

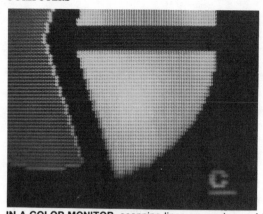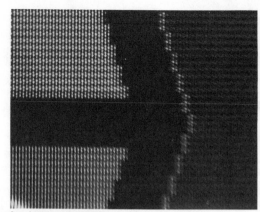

IN A COLOR MONITOR, scanning lines are made up of triads of red, green, and blue dots etched on the face of the tube. In the closeup (right) you can see how each dot in the triad is illuminated at a different intensity. This results in colors other than red, green and blue of the dots on the tube.

sharpness of the picture. The brighter you turn up these controls, the harder the electron beam hits the phosphor. This creates dots with bigger halos and less sharpness.

Some monitors have a window-screen-like mesh attached to the front. This is an anti-glare shield and its very effective in eliminating annoying reflection. It's available built-in to both monochrome and color monitors or can be added as an accessory later. Some of these anti-glare screens can create an optical resolution loss because the brightness control is turned up to compensate for the light filtered out.

Cost is a factor we all consider. Monochrome models range from $99 to about $250, and color models retail from $300 to $700. If you prefer, you can spend thousands of dollars on a color RGB display device designed for special scientific uses, but it's not likely that you'll find such units in your department or computer store.

THE DATA GENERAL/ONE™ (above) features a full-size liquid-crystal display monitor in a 10-pound portable package.

New technology breakthroughs

The fall of 1985 saw several lap-sized computers introduced with full 80 column, 25 line monochrome display screens less than an inch thick. These larger flat screens are a second generation of the 40 by 8 displays vying for acceptance in the computer marketplace for the past year or so. These screens use a technology called liquid-crystal-display (LCD)—something you've seen on pocket calculators and digital watches for a long time but just recently perfected to the point where they can be used as television screens or computer displays.

Two factors have affected their limited acceptance in the computer community: First, they had (until now) limited screen capacity. They were also limited to a monochrome display, and that often a very coarse matrix of dots or pixels.

Getting a workable liquid-crystal display (LCD) image on a monochrome screen was child's play compared to getting it in color. Unlike regular TV tubes, an LCD display doesn't generate its own light, so an external light source is needed. LCD watches and clocks have a tiny light bulb that reflects its light from the front of the crystal display. The technology for the LCD color TV was developed by Seiko and the company holds all patents for the sandwich-type television screen.

In the Epson Elf and the Seiko TFT (Thin Film Technology), transmitted light is used instead of reflected light. Light coming from a built-in fluorescent bulb, or reflected from a fold-down mirror, passes through the LCD elements. The screen uses polarized light to operate. Light coming through the rear glass of the screen's sandwich is filtered into parallel light waves by passing through the glass' polarizing structure. The light can be stopped by another screen or screen element that is polarized at a 90° angle.

The tiny TV's 2-inch (diagonal measure) screen is made up of 52,800 pixels or picture elements, and each of these is a fast-acting liquid-crystal element. The manufacturer has gone to great lengths to develop a special invisible transistor that's mounted on each picture element. This transistor provides the voltage to change the crystal's alignment to polarize the light in about 300 milliseconds (thousandths of a second). The transistors are indeed invisible, or at least transparent, and are deposited as thin films on the LCD elements. According to the manufacturer, each transistor is only 0.3 microns thick.

Each of the screen elements has a color filter in front—one for the three primary TV colors of red, blue and green. These in turn are grouped in threes, and each group is a triad.

Light shining through the screen from behind passes through one of these positions, and the filter gives that element its particular color. Where color is not called for (image is supposed to be dark), the LCD element electronically rotates its axis 90° and the light is blocked by the second polarizer.

The light source can be ordinary daylight, reflected from a fold-down mirror, or it can come from an internal fluorescent source, which you can switch on as needed. The battery drain is considerably lower when the set is sun-powered (1.1 watts vs. 1.9 watts in the Epson Elf).

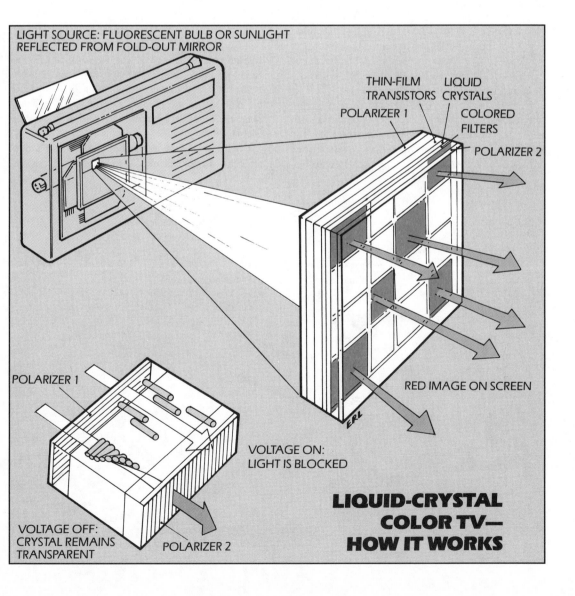

LIGHT SOURCE: FLUORESCENT BULB OR SUNLIGHT REFLECTED FROM FOLD-OUT MIRROR

THIN-FILM TRANSISTORS
LIQUID CRYSTALS
POLARIZER 1
COLORED FILTERS
POLARIZER 2

RED IMAGE ON SCREEN

POLARIZER 1

VOLTAGE ON: LIGHT IS BLOCKED

VOLTAGE OFF: CRYSTAL REMAINS TRANSPARENT

POLARIZER 2

LIQUID-CRYSTAL COLOR TV— HOW IT WORKS

Flat-screen displays

■ COMPUTERS MUST HAVE quick-changing displays if their true interactive properties are to be tapped. At the very beginning, computers depended on printers for virtually all their output. You typed in your input and waited until the output could be printed out on paper. The results were often maddeningly slow. The development of the familiar cathode ray tube (CRT) with its greenish (or sometimes amber or white) lettering was a tremendous step forward. The high-quality video monitor (and its less accurate kin, the conventional TV set) was another valuable advance because it allowed elaborate, even full-colored, graphic displays to be quickly projected.

Each of these electronic display devices is, in effect, a projector and screen in a sealed bottle (or tube). As with any projection system, there has to be a considerable throw distance between the lens and the screen surface if the picture is to be

big enough to be viewed comfortably. While the throw distance of a movie theater becomes mere inches inside a display tube, monitor design always requires the display device itself to be at least as deep as the beam throw—that is, several inches thick.

For many years, computer users—and video viewers—have yearned for a better electronic

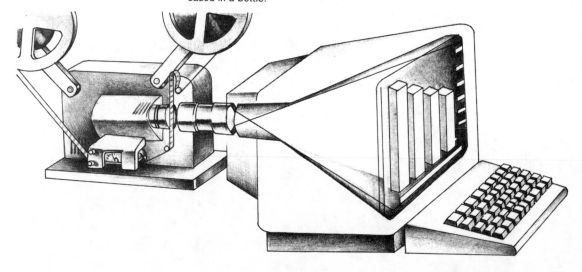

A CONVENTIONAL "picture tube" shows how it is really a miniature projector and screen system encased in a bottle.

Even so, these first-generation flat screens are remarkable achievements—and for many buyers, well worth their higher costs. The ability to take them out into the real world, without having a wheelbarrow for transport, is a tremendous technological advance.

But because of their various limitations and shortcomings, the current crop of flat screens is rarely used to replace conventional electronic display tube devices in offices, homes and schools. The demand for an effective and economical flat screen is still to be met. To consider the prospects for replacing the conventional tube within the next few years requires an examination of the types, problems and possibilities.

Flat screens can be manufactured from any of four different display technologies: liquid crystal (LCD), vacuum fluorescent (VFD), gas plasma (GPD), and electroluminescent (ELD).

Liquid crystal display (LCD) flat screens

LCD technology is well known thanks to its widespread use in digital wristwatches, calculators and pocket TV sets. LCD screens, usually small, work fairly well except that the gray scale is very limited and they must be viewed at a very critical angle and away from direct sunlight to be seen at all.

The chief problem with LCDs is that they do not emit light. Their images are formed by applying tiny electric currents to the numerous liquid crystal cells that make up the dot-matrixed screen. Some cells become darkened in order to form letters, numbers or graphic shapes. Other cells remain neutral-colored as a means of showing a contrasting background.

The resulting displays require ambient light to be read, very much like a printed page. But because the liquid crystal structures are encased behind a smooth glass screen, they are visually wiped out if the light comes at a reflective angle. For these reasons, the LCD format is not considered a major contender in the flat screen sweepstakes.

Other screen contenders

The vacuum fluorescent (VFD) technology is useful only in small-scale metering displays. It offers little possibility for the larger display screens computer users, at home or afield, are clamoring for.

That leaves the gas plasma and electroluminescent systems, which are actually rather similar technologies. Both emit their own light; the difference between them is the source of that light.

THE NEW FLAT-SCREEN microcomputers are small enough to hold in your lap—and to take aboard a plane in a briefcase.

display technology. They want a screen that is flat (or, at least, very thin) and can be folded away when desired. One that does not become very hot to the touch, is lightweight, long-lasting, easy to maintain, battery "powerable" and easy to read. They will accept monochrome if they must, but prefer full-color capacity.

It's been a tall order for the technological community—too tall for quick satisfaction. But progress has been made, and more is yet to come.

Nowadays, the flat screen, mostly in rather primitive forms, is a highly visible market item. The portable lap computer has brought the technology out of the laboratory and into the showroom. A number of models are available, all relatively expensive—with some of the better ones in the very expensive category.

Higher-priced portable models with flat, foldable screens provide more columns and rows as well as greater detail. They can be used for high-resolution graphing or game-playing. But only in monochrome; color is yet to come in standard market models.

The current models all share certain problems. They are not only rather costly compared to regular CRT screens but also lack brilliance and detail. Moreover, most of them must be viewed in shadowed environments; otherwise they appear washed out. The angle of viewing is also critical. A shift too far to the side or top can cause the same sort of visual wash-out as you get from too much direct light on the screen.

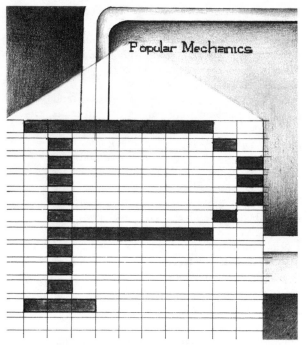

A PIXEL is a picture element found at the row and column coordinates of a computer screen. The more of these there are, the higher the resolution.

In GPD technology, the light comes from the ionization of a gas—usually neon or a mixture of neon and argon—stored between a set of charged electrodes.

In ELD screens, the emitted light results from the stimulation of a solid luminescent material placed between a pair of charged electrodes.

General flat screen design characteristics

The flat screens of both light-emitting systems are designed around the familiar pixel-grid concept which is also used in LCD screens. A grid screen consists of a large number of light points called picture elements, or pixels. Each pixel can be addressed by coordinates that represent the junctions of columns and rows on the screen.

The more pixels there are, the more detailed the screen picture can be. A screen formated into a distinct dot-matrix pattern is excellent for routine alphanumeric displays. High-resolution graphic displays require a fully populated screen matrix—one with an enormously greater number of pixels per inch. Not surprisingly, there is a tremendous cost difference between the two types of screen displays. Most computer users prefer the latter.

If each pixel had to be lighted (that is, electrified) separately, the screen circuit systems would be a nightmarish maze of wires. To get around this, designers have used the grid, or matrix. The electric current required to activate a given pixel is provided by additive voltage feeds along the column and row at whose juncture the pixel falls. Any pixel receiving voltage from both column and row sources gets enough voltage to light up. Others remain dark.

A CRT screen customarily uses luminescent materials that play to the human phenomenon called "persistence of vision"—the tendency of a lighted object to remain visible to the viewer for a short time after its illumination actually disappears. If such an effect did not occur, the displays would seem to flicker as a consequence of the rapidly successive "on/off" voltage feeds used to compose individual screen matrices, pixel by pixel.

Design of the more sophisticated video monitors (and regular TV screens) is based on the same physiological principles. These display devices depend on an internal scanning system to line-paint the screen images in successive frames not unlike those on a movie film.

Keeping an individual pixel lighted after its initial voltage turn-on is a problem for the flat-screen designer. If each pixel in a complex graphic display has to be separately activated each time the screen is electrically recomposed—and that happens many times each second—the system will become overburdened and sluggish. An answer has been found in the use of screen structures that will remain lighted after being electrically toggled to become so. Or, conversely, will stay darkened in the same way. This process has been termed "bistable memory."

Gas plasma display (GPD) flat screens

GPD gas plasma systems generally fall into two technical categories: those operated by direct current (DC) and those by alternating current (AC).

Both types act on luminescent gas stored at low pressure in a thin glass chamber sealed between a pair of (often transparent) electrodes. Electrons of the gas are energized by a high-voltage field. They momentarily disassociate from their own atomic structures into a so-called plasma state. As they quickly return to a lower-energy condition, they cause the release of glowing reddish-orange photons.

The simpler DC type of GPD screen consists of a glass-encased grid of gas chambers, each at a pixel position. Electrical connections, called nodes, at each position are connected to column and row voltage feeds. A spacer plate having a straightforward dot matrix format separates the opposing electrodes. The design works well except that it will not permit bistable memory, necessitating continuous, total pixel activation. This is a distinct disadvantage when complex screen configurations are to be shown.

The more complex AC systems make use of a dielectric (nonconductive) layer between the gas and each of the electrodes. In effect, each gas chamber becomes a tiny capacitor that can temporarily store electrical power from incoming AC signals, using this power to hold its state while waiting for the next voltage to come to it. It is this

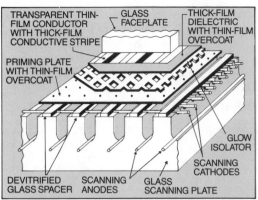

A VARIANT of the gas plasma screen has been developed by Burroughs Corp. It combines AC-DC formats in one unit.

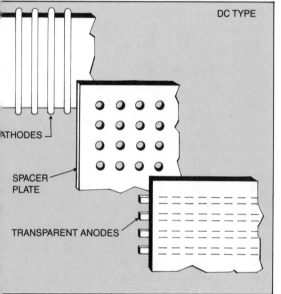

S PLASMA display allows electric currents to ize neon in a matrixed glass chamber.

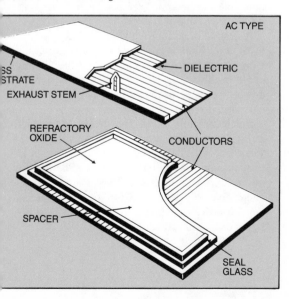

valuable characteristic that gives the AC design its bistable memory. AC power applied directly to the gas itself provides the necessary toggling action required to turn pixels on and off for longer than fractional intervals.

One promising GPD design, developed by the Burroughs Corporation, actually makes use of both AC and DC forms. This hybrid scheme links the electrical drive simplicity of the DC type to the image memory of the AC units. The DC system primes the gas to make it more responsive to the required ionization. The AC component permits easier pixel control.

GPD screens tend to be extraordinarily expensive, although in certain applications they actually outperform and significantly outlast high-quality CRTs and video screens. The higher voltages necessary also add certain problems to their widespread application.

Research on GPD formats continues. There is hope that costs may tumble from a couple of thousand down to a couple of hundred dollars per 80x25 screen. Color displays are also seen as a real possibility. The power requirements, especially in portable (battery) applications, do not yet seem susceptible to easy solutions, however.

Electroluminescent (ELD) flat screens

The strongest candidate for flat-screen market supremacy is the electroluminescent display (ELD) format.

The ELD has been called the solid-state alternative to the GPD. This is because the luminescence doesn't come from gas photons but from a solid phosphorescent material that responds to electrical stimulation.

While there are at least four varieties of ELD design now on the market, they all involve enclosing a thin electroluminescent slab between two dielectric slices that in turn have been bracketed by opposing electrode plates. The whole sandwich is encased in glass. This most commonly encountered luminescent chemical is zinc sulfide doped with manganese or other substances. The energizing processes are almost ex-actly like that of the AC and DC GPD systems discussed before. Bistable, keep-alive memory at each pixel is possible with the AC version. Picture brightness is notably less than that of the GPD forms, although still at acceptable levels.

The cost of a good-quality ELD flat-screen (40x25) is around $700. A larger screen would, of course, be more expensive, but not nearly so steep as a corresponding GPD model. Power requirements are about half those of the GPDs, an important consideration in the design of portable computers. Durability is not the equal of that of the plasma devices at this time, however.

Proponents of the ELD flat screens believe that prices will come down very significantly over the next several years. They also suggest that full-color versions are likely. Some people see ELD screens as potentially useful for video and TV output.

The market outlook

Estimates range widely among the experts as to the length of time remaining before the general market sees high-quality flat screens that are reasonably priced (the same as or lower than the current CRT levels) and that have most or all of the desired features. A consensus seems to fall around five years, although it could be sooner if certain technical and manufacturing break-throughs were to occur. Volume sales can be counted on to bring prices down if the flat screen products really do what customers want.

One of the more important technological breakthroughs in the flat-screen field came recently in the development of new microchips that can handle the higher voltage patterns of the several light-emitting forms. This may well eliminate one of the more serious barriers to mass development and marketing.

A desired breakthrough would be an improvement in the light emissions of the ELD forms and a corresponding way of eliminating the viewing angle problems. Users don't like to be pinned down to a single head position, as they are with current flat-screen technologies.

Screen fragility is yet another issue that will require some laboratory miracles. Glass cases work, but if the flat screen is made strong enough to withstand normal handling in a classroom or out in the field, the glass enclosures are apt to become relatively weighty. Perhaps a transparent new plastic can be developed—one that is tough, lightweight and scratch-resistant.

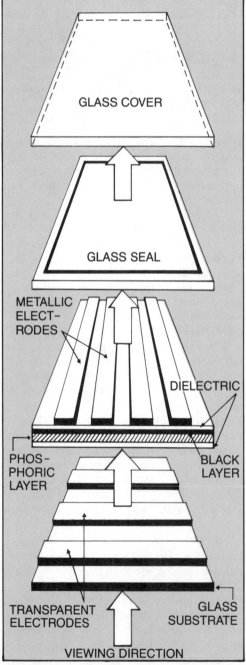

IN AN ELD SCREEN, the phosphorescent layer lights up when voltage is applied through matrixed electrodes.

Potentials

It is fair to say that the development of a practical, low-cost flat screen will mean more than just an improved replacement for CRTs, video monitors and TV sets. Consider the consequences in public education, for example.

Schools across the country have begun to equip themselves with lots of microcomputers. This is to enable their students to become more computer-literate and, far more importantly, to puter power in study areas like mathematics, science and word processing. Aside from cost, some of the very serious inhibitions to computerizing classrooms are the size, heat production, maintenance problems and handling awkwardness of present-day computer terminals with their heavy CRTs or video monitors. A classroom filled with microcomputer terminals at every student desk is a forest of bulky technology. Among other problems, the teacher literally loses eye contact with students, and vice versa.

Suppose a school terminal included an inexpensive, durable, lightweight flat screen that could actually be folded away into a desk-top console, along with a foldable keyboard. Computers could be used by students and teachers almost as comfortably as pencils and paper—and without cluttering up the room with bulky, heat-producing monitors.

At the university level, and out in the business world, the flat panel screen could revolutionize the ways in which computers are used for word processing, data handling and figure manipulation. People would be able to make use of computers in class or at work as they often do now, but they could also take computers along home or to the library where their low-profile presence would greatly intensify their ultimate utility. A panel screen attached to a truly portable console containing its own high-memory capacities could make the micro into an instrument of daily communication as common as books and paper.

It should be noted that the electronic display devices currently in use are not only the largest components of most computer systems, they are also likely to be among the more expensive. If the flat, foldable panel is to become the pervasive screen display form, it must reverse these tendencies.

There is strong reason to believe that the flat screen will meet these challenges and come into operational prominence before too many years pass.

WITHOUT FLAT-SCREEN displays, computers in the classroom are bulky units interfering with eye contact and communication between students and teacher.

Communicating with computers

■ ONE OF THE great moments in the history of computers occurred when it was realized that computers should communicate. This meant they could share programs and data with each other—and thousands of individual user terminals linked in through ordinary telephone lines.

Industry was quick to exploit the new possibilities. For example, a terminal at the ticket counter of one airline at a particular airport could be used not only to book flights with that company's own mainframe (i.e. large-scale) computer back at headquarters; it could also make reservations directly with the networked computers of other airline companies across the country as well. The savings in time and labor—and customer satisfaction—were enormous.

But this single example of telecommunicating computers didn't stop there. It was soon realized that travel agencies in every city and town could also be connected in to the new booking network. Flight reservations in each airline's own computers could be made and confirmed from thousands and thousands of different locations. Even large airline users, such as giant corporations and government agencies, were sometimes allowed to bridge terminals into the system as a means of expediting their own flight plans.

Then came the historic development of microcomputers, the smaller computers you could use at home as well as at work or school. These new devices could also be used as computer terminals. Special new arrangements were made by the airline industry to permit individual computer owners to dial in to the reservation system through any one of a number of telephone-accessed data exchanges, using their personal credit card numbers as billing addresses. Now flight information and reservations could be al-

THIS TERMINAL at an airline ticket counter is connected by telephone lines to the computers of many different companies.

THE MODEM can be used with any telephone anywhere and allows a wide range of new communications possibilities that voice contact with home or the home office can't.

most instantaneously transacted with hundreds of thousands—even millions—of scattered locations!

How computers communicate

Regardless of the transmitting medium used, both private and public computer communications involve the same basic process.

The *digital* signals generated by a sending computer (mainframe or micro) are converted into *analog* signals so they can be transmitted through linking circuit systems to a receiving computer (mainframe or micro). Then the incoming analog signals are reconverted into digital form again so the computer can deal with them.

Digital signals in a computer are characterized by their binary (or Base 2) form. They are either "on" or "off." The binary numbers that these simple signals build are the basis for all the complex mathematical and data manipulations of which the computer is capable.

Ordinary telephone circuits—or most other telecommunications pathways—cannot transmit binary signals directly. They lack the required accuracy and speed. These conventional electronic links are designed to send analog signals.

Analog signals are actually much more complex than binary ones. They consist of wave forms, usually having a fluctuating sine wave (or roller coaster) appearance when shown on a wave form monitor. The wave forms represent (are analogous to) the complex sound frequencies of the sorts that make up voices and music.

While analog signals are electronically more complex than binary ones, they are also much less accurate. This doesn't matter so much in the case of natural sound reproduction. The inevitable distortions in the analog wave forms, resulting from inaccurate transmission channels and other factors, usually don't do enough damage to prevent our recognizing what was intended, even on low-fidelity telephone lines.

But one single distorted bit in a binary signal can change an "on" to an "off," or vice versa. And that can alter the signal's meaning in a profound way. It can render a message meaningless to a computer that operates only on perfect binary signals.

Accuracy of transmission also often involves the speed of delivery as well as the bandwidth of the circuit used. Think of the problem in terms of a liquid traveling through a pipe. The bigger the pipe, the more liquid that can pass through a certain length during a given interval of time. Or,

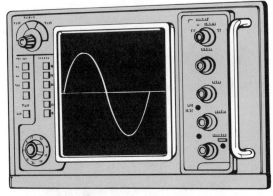

ANALOG SIGNALS tend to have a sine wave form that resembles a roller-coaster.

conversely, the longer the time, the more liquid that can pass through the length of a given pipe size.

The broader the bandwidth of a circuit (that is, the more Hertzes, or cycles, it makes available), the more of a message that can pass through in a given interval of time. Or, conversely, the longer the interval, the more of a message that can pass through a given circuit bandwidth.

Digital signals fed out from a computer travel at tremendously high speeds. Therefore, the circuits they move through must be wide in order to accommodate them. If the circuits lack the necessary bandwidth, the signals must be slowed down to longer intervals. If this step were not taken, crippling signal inaccuracies would result.

LARGER SATELLITE DISHES are used to pick up high-density telecommunications sent through air and space.

THE MIGHTY MODEM comes in many sizes, capacities and prices, but all allow computer to communicate through ordinary telephone circuits.

The mighty modem

When conventional analog telecommunications circuits are used to link computers, the outgoing digital signals must be transformed into analog wave shapes. This is done with a device called a modulator. Then when the analog signal is converted back into a digital form, a device called a demodulator is used. The two devices mounted together, which is the conventional arrangement, is called a *modem* (**MOD**ulator-**DE**-Modulator). A modem can be used to send and receive computer data.

What the modem does to transmit the digital data is simple. It changes the high-speed digital signals into analog waves representing only two distinct sounds. One frequency represents "on" and another "off." These two analog frequencies travel along conventional narrow-band circuits at very much slower rates than the computer spews out the originating digital signals on which they are based. Therefore, the modem (or the com-

puter itself) must have special capacities with which it can buffer the outgoing messages—that is, hold them in temporary storage until they can be released bit by bit along the much slower analog circuits.

If you were to listen to a computer message traveling along an analog telephone circuit, you would hear only "bloops and bleeps" representing the original binary codes from which they derive, and to which they will soon return.

Once the computer message reaches its destination, the receiving modem reverses things. It takes the analog frequencies and translates them back into digital signals. Buffer capacities are used to allow a sufficient supply of binary code to collect before feeding it forward into the waiting computer's input port.

What happens at this point depends on commands issued through special telecommunications software already loaded into the computer being used.

You may choose to have the incoming material displayed on the display screen to be read as soon as it arrives.

Or you may choose to have it print out directly on an attached printer so you can read the hard copy at your convenience.

Or you may choose to have it down-loaded onto a floppy diskette (or hard disk) associated with the computer. Then later on, you could call it onto the display screen, have it printed out, or both. (This alternative is called a "spool"—an acronym derived from **S**imultaneous **P**eripheral **O**perations **O**n **L**ine. Not all telecommunications software programs provide for spooling, however.)

The circuits used to connect computers are ordinarily full-duplex links. They can be used for

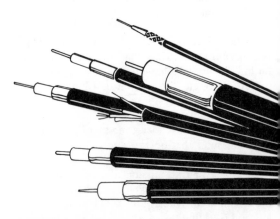

COAXIAL CABLE is a flexible tube in which one conductor is a sleeve that completely encircles the other, which is a wire.

sending and receiving without manually switching between the two modes, just as with a two-way telephone conversation. A half-duplex system requires mode switching, as when conversing by CB radios. A simplex system is used for one-way communication, as with a broadcast.

Modems are not all alike, by any means. Virtually all contemporary modems are full-duplex or half-duplex. The simplest ones will require you to switch (manually) between sending and receiving. The more complex will do such switching automatically. Moreover, the top line modems will answer incoming calls without human intervention. They can be programmed through the attached computer to make outgoing calls on a time schedule as well.

Costs for modems range from about $50 to $1,000, depending on features, quality and speed. These costs usually cover not only the modem hardware but also the associated communications software.

Transmission speeds

Analog transmissions of computer messages are generally slower than digital relays. It is also true that analog speed can be varied under certain circumstances.

The simpler modems use a speed of 300 baud, under a convention established some years ago by the telephone companies. A "baud" is a term meaning "bits per second." Most microcomputers have their binary bits organized into bytes of 8 bits each. A byte usually represents one alphabetic or numerical character. Therefore, a 300-baud modem will allow some 36 characters to be transmitted each second. That sounds fast—almost too fast to read on a display screen. But actually, in computing terms, it's very, very slow. An output buffer has lots of work to do to store signals until they can be fed out one by one. An input buffer is practically out of business!

More elaborate modems will also permit speeds of 1200, 4800 or even 9600 baud. Not only do these devices cost more themselves, but the telephone circuits used for the higher delivery rates must be of a much more accurate sort. The circuits must be technically conditioned in various ways to improve fidelity and reduce analog distortions. Often they must also offer wider bandwidths in order to facilitate the higher speeds. Wideband and conditioned circuits cost considerably more than regular telephone lines.

It's true, however, that many computer users actually find it cheaper to use the more sophisticated, high-speed systems. That's because of the relatively high cost of conventional long-distance telephone lines. A 300-baud transmission may take 15 minutes to execute while a 9600-baud feed can reduce the time to less than a minute. Over a period of weeks or months, the savings in long-distance charges can often pay for the more elaborate modem—and then some.

Ways of communicating

The communications software that accompanies a sophisticated modem will usually permit the sending computer to upload materials to receiving computers having comparable communications capacities. This means that you can send a message—or a program—to another computer, even if it's unattended. This is an essential arrangement if you are interested in sending or receiving so-called "electronic mail."

But there are, in fact, other simpler but nonetheless useful forms of electronic message exchanging.

The basic process involves calling the receiving source on the telephone and asking for the computer at that location to have its modem plugged in to the telephone line so the message can be sent, with or without keyboard replies. (An older, more trouble-prone form of modem called an acoustic coupler actually allowed the telephone handset to be cradled snugly inside a set of rubber listening cups which picked up with analog "bloops and bleeps" and relayed them on into the waiting computer.)

THIS DEVICE, called a modem, is used to communicate with other computers by ordinary telephone lines.

Sometimes, the two computers in question have to go through a series of special hand-shaking protocols to determine the technical parameters necessary for the interchange to take place at all. The two units are required to be set to the same baud rates and byte lengths, among other factors.

A helpful variant on the call-up procedure involves use of what might be termed a "data exchange" as an intermediary. A data exchange is a mainframe computer used to store and relay messages and information to many users. Most such services are operated commercially, although computer users groups in some communities have established such services called "bulletin boards," using large micros as the host computers.

With a data exchange, you dial up the host computer, which has automatic connection capacities in its own multiple modems. Then, by following a prescribed set of key-in steps, you are fed a menu from which you can choose to "download" or "upload" messages. In the former situation, you are switched to a sort of "electronic mailbox," which shows whether you have actually received any messages since last you called in. If you have, you type in a formal download request, adjust your modem to receive (if that is required), and in a few moments in come the stored materials bearing your name or number. (Number codes are sometimes used to protect privacy.)

If you want to leave a message for another computer having access to the same data exchange, you type in the necessary commands and upload the message that you had previously prepared on your word processor. It will be stored in the mainframe until the recipient calls in for it.

These data exchanges are also useful for many other services. It has already been mentioned that airline reservations can be made through them. So can many other transactions, such as ordering mail order products or buying computer games and software programs.

Moreover, these facilities—of which the two best known are The Source in McLean, Virginia, and Compuserve in Columbus, Ohio—will give you access to all manner of informational data bases like newswires, stock quotations, weather forecasts and research findings. In fact, whole encyclopedias have been stored in electronic formats so that people can use them for ready reference. They are likely to be much more up to date than conventional encyclopedia books because new facts can be entered on a daily basis instead of waiting for annual printings.

The commercial data exchanges earn their revenues from membership fees. Some are paid up front, others use by use. Most of these modern information "utilities" make systematic use of special, lower-cost telephone circuits. But even so, you can expect a hefty charge for time on line—unless you conduct your transactions during the middle of the night when long-distance rates are minuscule.

A new possibility

An interesting variation of the two-way data exchange is being planned in various parts of the country. Analog data signals will be hidden away (or multiplexed) in the carrier waves of radio and TV broadcasts. Special off-air modems of a simplex design will pull in the low cost, addressable messages to subscribing computers. Since these new data services will be only one way, a conventional telephone modem will have to be used to call in informational requests or to answer inquiries. Even so, this may be cheaper than using expensive long-distance telephone circuits for both sides of the communications exchange.

Schools have indicated a great interest in this technology because it would permit state departments of education to send out massive quantities of useful instructional software to many school buildings at once at a fraction of the cost of other distribution methods. Other government agencies are also looking closely at the potentials of transmitting widely used administrative documentation through such a system.

Yet interestingly enough, this "new" idea has been used before. Radio Nederland in Holland regularly sends out computer programs to its listeners around the world over its short-wave services. In this instance, the analog tones are not hidden away deep inside the carrier wave where they can't be detected by regular audiences. They are broadcast right over the main channel for all to hear! Computers pick up the signals with cassette tape recorders. Needless to say, reception has to be very good if the receiving recorders are to capture all the binary code required for proper digital use in the computer.

A common language

This brings us around to the matter of program coding in computer communications.

In the best of circumstances, two computers can send and receive any language coding that they both use. The choices are wide: BASIC, FORTRAN, ASSEMBLY, COBOL—you name it. But both computers must be equipped to use exactly the same language coding. For all practical purposes, this is very apt to mean that the computers themselves must be the same types and models.

What happens if the computers are different, which is actually true in most cases? The computers involved can communicate only in text. Computer programs in languages like BASIC and FORTRAN cannot be used. This is really not as limiting as it may sound. Most computerists don't engage in much programming of their own anyway. They are more concerned with messages than with process.

The trick is to have the sending computer convert all the text materials into what is called ASCII code—(American Standard Code for Information Interchange)—which, in fact, they are very likely to be in to start with.

ASCII text is made up of letters, numbers and punctuation marks formed of bytes that have the same binary values from computer to computer regardless of brand or model. Word-processing, data-base and spreadsheet programs customarily provide means for turning their outputs into ASCII (pronounced AS-key) formats.

The receiving computer can read the ASCII text without problems, although some coded command elements like carriage returns and line feeds occasionally become mangled through nonstandard assignments. When this happens, paragraphs and page breaks may not pan out, causing the text to run on continuously or with odd spaces appearing here and there. Yet the meanings of the words themselves are rarely affected.

While coded programming cannot be exchanged between different sorts of computers, the incoming ASCII text materials (customarily called "files") can often be fitted into data bases, spreadsheets or word-processing programs native to the receiving computer. This happy fact has done much to reduce the anxieties about the absence of compatibility between, and among, most mainframes and micros.

Security

Recently there has been a fair amount of concern over the fact that microcomputer owners—youngsters and adults—can use modem commu-

A SINGLE FIBER is capable of carrying over 6,000 simultaneous conversations. The copper cable carries only 2,400 conversations.

nications to break into mainframe computing centers in commerce, industry, government and the military. While the problem may have been a bit overdramatized in the news and Hollywood movies, it is perfectly true that such a thing can happen. It does take great (if sadly misguided) skill, patience and luck to accomplish, however. Furthermore, it's getting harder all the time.

Absolute computer security is difficult, if not impossible, to guarantee as long as the machine in question is linked to outside communications circuits. But relative and practical security is not. The use of various control numbers to limit access works pretty well if the numbers are complex—and random. Trying to have people use their birth dates, anniversaries or social security numbers as a computer combination invites logical deductions in tampering by the misguided gifted.

The outlook

Most technological specialists believe that the computer is as important a telecommunications instrument as the telephone and radio. Its ability to send complex data in hard-copy, electronically storable forms makes it a wholly different kind of information medium. Their confident prediction is that most people will use computer communications as often as they do the telephone within a decade or so.

Computer system hookups

■ CONNECTOR CABLES for your printer and modem can cost a bundle. Here's how to make your own.

You need connecting cables so your computer can talk to its peripherals. The price tag on these cables often induces shock in first-time computer buyers. A typical 10-ft. connector cable that marries an IBM-type computer to a parallel printer might cost you nearly $50 ready-made. You can make it for about half the price.

Degrees of difficulty

Building a cable set from flat ribbon is child's play if you're making a straight-through hookup, where the pin numbers from one connector go to the same numbers on another. This occurs when you're mating compatible components—say, D-type to D-type (a 25-pin serial connection for communications modems and some printers) or Centronics-type to Centronics (a 36-pin parallel connection for printers). Unfortunately, not all cables are this simple. A good example is the $50 cable used to connect popular IBM-type computers to printers of many brands.

Only one end of that cable requires a D-type connector to match the 25-pin output of IBM computers, while the other end needs a 36-pin connector to fit the Centronics-type input now standard on most printers. In this case, you have to study the technical manuals to determine which pin numbers match up at each end. The pin-matching sequence for the IBM parallel is diagrammed here.

Before you buy parts for your cable, check your computer equipment to determine whether female or male connectors are required (male connectors have multiple pins; females have a series of holes into which the pins are inserted). Also, buy 25-conductor flat-ribbon cables for D-type connections; 36-conductor for Centronics connections and 25-conductor for D-type to Centronics hookups.

Simple connections

Most straight-through flat-ribbon cable connectors require just one tool for assembly—a bench vise. The connectors contain two rows of V-shaped, fingerlike contacts. Each one of these contacts grabs its own wire and holds it separately from the adjacent wire in the ribbon cable. Some connectors come with double-sided adhesive on the back piece (the part that pushes the cable into those V-shaped contacts) to help you position the ribbon cable before clamping the two halves together. This is a nice feature, which helps to keep the cable straight and in position.

Once you have the ribbon positioned and the two halves of the connector in place, hold it so the cable doesn't slip, put it between the jaws of a bench vise and tighten the vise until the back

WITH THIS CONNECTOR, you can attach flat-ribbon cable to the adhesive surface on pack piece (top) before assembly to help hold it in place while you work.

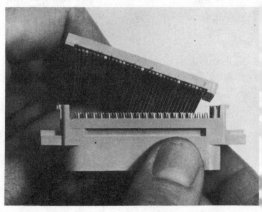

piece snaps into place and can go no farther. Repeat the process at the other end of the cable. Don't overtighten the vise: You might damage the connector.

Whenever you start one of the cable sets, find pin 1 on the connector and mark the No. 1 pin corner on the back of the connector with a red crayon so you can find it later. Most ribbon cables are gray except for a stripe of red ink down one edge. Put the red-striped edge into pin 1, and do the same at the other end. Some ribbon cable is rainbow-hued, with repeating sets of 10 different-colored wires, starting with brown. Brown is your No. 1 pin wire.

Many connectors label only pin 1: you have to figure out the others for yourself. Some connectors will have the four corner pin number labeled; sometimes all the pins are numbered. And you'll find some connectors that have no pin numbers at all.

Remember that male and female pin numbers are mirror images of each other, and they're mirror-reversed once again when you go from front to back of the connector.

Discrete wiring

Besides squeezing the ribbon cables in a vise, there are three other ways to attach the wires to the connector. All of them take more work and much more time. These other methods use discrete wiring—connecting the conductors one by one—so use this type of connector only when you must change pin connections (as when mating

T-HANDLE TOOL helps push separated wire conductors into the V-shaped slots in this connector. For 28-ga. wire, use color-coded connector with yellow dot.

D-type to Centronics connectors), or when you absolutely can't get straight-through, flat-ribbon cable connectors.

At some parts supply stores, you'll find that the connector supply consists almost entirely of D-types with solder-cup back lugs. Trouble is, flat-ribbon cable wires are super-skinny (22 to 28 ga.), and these connectors don't provide a convenient anchor point to bend the wires around. You have to strip the wire, tin the end, fill the connector pin cup with solder and slip the wire in. Hold the wire until the solder cools and locks it in place. You're working in close quarters here, so get the smallest tip you can find for your soldering iron.

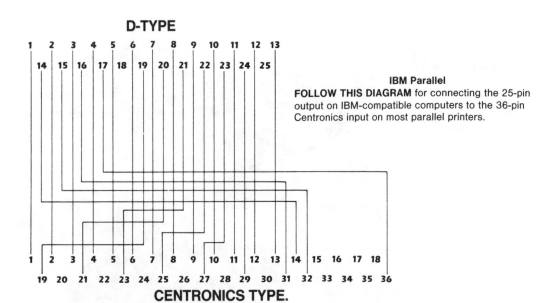

IBM Parallel
FOLLOW THIS DIAGRAM for connecting the 25-pin output on IBM-compatible computers to the 36-pin Centronics input on most parallel printers.

A second method uses individually inserted pins for D-type connectors, using either a friction fit for the wire or a barrel crimp. Some careful use of long-nose pliers will help you make these connections, although you can buy a special crimping tool. With this type of connector, you buy and empty connector shell and loose pins. You create your own D-type connector by filling in just those holes that you need with crimp-type pins.

The last discrete method uses a connector with double V-shaped contacts for each wire. For this, you need a special tool, a T-handle wire insertion tool, to press the wire firmly into those V slots. (Used carefully, a small-bladed screwdriver will do the job just about as well.) As with the vise-clamp technique, this connector requires no wire stripping; the pressure of insertion is all that is needed to shove the insulation back from the wire just where the contact is made. It's a really painless method of doing discrete wiring.

IBM connection

To make the IBM parallel connection, use a vise-type squeeze conductor for the male D-type that plugs into the computer. At the other end you'll need one of the T-handle male Centronics connectors, since the cable set has some odd wiring changes. The wiring diagram shown here shows which wires go where.

Note that pins 1 through 14 run to the same pin numbers (not to the same pin locations) on both connectors. It's when you get to pin 15 that the wiring sequence begins to change to a more complicated procedure.

When buying the T-handle connectors, check the V-notch size. There's a color-code dot in the middle of the connector's backside, which you may be able to see through the plastic polybag. You want yellow for working with 28-gauge ribbon cable. The other color codes are designed for larger wire diameters and just won't work at all with most sizes of ribbon cables.

Begin by peeling all 25 wires from each other for a space of about 2½ in. from the end that's going into the discrete connector. A piece of plastic tape around the ribbon 2½ in. from the end will keep the wires from peeling too far. Start each peel with a small nip from a pair of diagonal cutters. Pull each wire straight down (perpendicular to) the flat ribbon; do not pull wires apart sideways. This will give you good peeling action and keep the conductor's insulation intact.

Remember that when working with ribbon wires, the first one (red stripe) will be coming from pin 1 on the D-type connector; the next wire will be coming from pin 14, then pin 2, then pin 15, then pin 3 and so on. This sequence is shown by the rows of upper and lower numbers on our diagram. Although the discrete connector is designed for a round, plastic-jacketed multiwire cable, you can tape the ends of the individual ribbon wires you've pulled apart so they fit nicely.

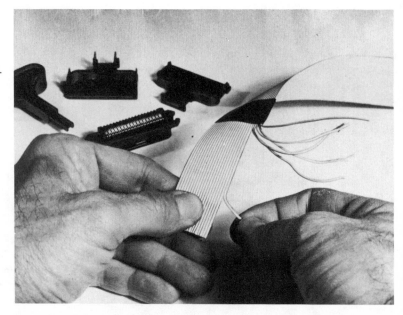

WHEN SEPARATING CONDUCTORS, place a piece of tape 2½ in. from the end to prevent peeling.

Computer care and repair

■ THE MICROCOMPUTER is a remarkable machine. It takes very little effort to care for it on a day-to-day basis. It has relatively few moving parts to wear out or lose alignment. Even so, a computer and its peripherals do require some trouble-prevention care. This is especially true with diskette and cassette systems that do have critical mechanical components.

Never feed a computer

Never bring food or liquids to the computer table. One accidental spill of a soft drink or cup of coffee can cripple a microcomputer. A handful of crumbs in the wrong place can also wreak havoc of a very expensive kind to parts like the disk drives.

Don't leave fingerprints

Not only should snacks be kept safely away from the keyboard and peripherals at all times, but so should greasy, wet or sticky hands. A messy fingerprint on a computer key doesn't look nice; one left on a floppy disk or cassette can wipe out valuable programs and data. A sloppy fingerprint can foul up a drive mechanism to the point of requiring a major repair. (Actually, *any* fingerprint placed on the surface of a disk or cassette is bad. Natural oils in the skin can do almost as much damage as gunk from a careless snack. Make it a rule never to touch recording surfaces—with clean hands or otherwise!)

Duck a shocking enemy

No less dangerous to computer health is the unseen, but not always unfelt, menace of ordinary static electricity. This is the familiar spark generated by scuffing your shoes on carpets during wintertime, with its lowered indoor humidity readings.

If a static electric charge reaches one of the microchips inside the console of computer, it can cause mysterious data loses, blackouts or even serious component damage. You do not have to touch the effected chip directly. A harmful elec-

A COMPUTER DISASTER WAITING TO HAPPEN A computer workstation like this is asking for trouble. Drinks on computer table can spill into the keyboard, making keys a sticky mess; cookie crumbs can eventually stop proper key action; chocolate fingerprints on keys or disks can gum up sensitive mechanisms; disks strewn around are inviting valuable data loss, even destruction; strong household cleaners can permanently damage the CRT or computer's plastic case.

PUT FLOPPY DISKS back in protective cases to guard against dust, heat distortion and bending.

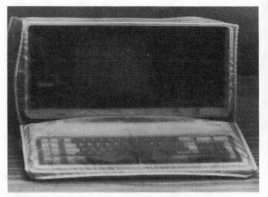

WHEN NOT IN USE, protect against dust with a cover. Dust covers are also available to cover only the keyboard.

tric shock can be relayed through metal parts leading from the exterior of the console case.

There are several things you can do to avoid this risk. Keep the humidity of the computer area to an acceptable 40%-50% level with a small inexpensive humidifier. But care is required. Too much humidity is also bad; the condensed moisture can lead to corrosion within the computer system.

One of the most effective techniques is also the cheapest. You can approach the computer with a metal key in hand, carefully touching it to some nearby metallic surface *not* connected to the computer itself *before* placing your hands on the keyboard or console. This will send any accumulated static electricity harmlessly to ground before it can damage or destroy sensitive components.

You can buy special anti-static mats from computer stores to place under your chair. These neutralize static buildup. They are not cheap, however. Obviously, a tile or wood floor in the computer area can also minimize the risk of a problem.

Let it be neither too hot nor too cold

Heat and cold also pose potential problems for computers and the recording media used in them. Take care that your "rig" (including the diskette or cassette files) is not allowed to wilt in high heat or shiver in the cold. As a rule, computer systems should be kept in room conditions "fit for a human."

Floppy disks face special dangers from temperature extremes or direct sunlight. The plastic materials they're made of can become distorted or warped, making them unplayable. Keep disks away from these adverse conditions. Computer cassettes are only slightly more durable. Protect them as well.

Give special care to disks and cassettes

The handling of floppy disks and cassettes also requires care to avoid frustrating data losses. Always keep disks inside their protective paper envelopes when they are not being used. Even in the midst of a hot and heavy computing session, diskettes or cassettes should not be strewn or piled around computer work surfaces. A scratch, a rub—even worse, a crease—inflicted by a hasty accident can devastate the data and ruin the recording medium.

Make it a regular habit to put disks or cassettes back into their proper storage bins, boxes or cases when not needed inside the drive. The storage spaces themselves should be designed so that the disks or cassettes are not subject to dust, heat, internal bending or excessive moisture. Nor should they be located near to active magnetic fields. Magnetic impulses from closeby telephones, loudspeakers or transformers can erase disk or cassette tracks without warning.

Labeling disks or cassettes is also a good-care habit to be cultivated. Recording over valuable data by mistake can be painful and costly.

Watch that power

Unpredictable—and usually invisible—power surges or spikes in the electric current of an ordinary AC wall socket can destroy internal computer components. Ordinary home appliances on the same circuits may be wholly unaffected. As a prudent user, you should never plug a computer system directly into normal house current.

It should be a hard and fast rule that any computer system receive its electric power only through a *surge/spike protector*. These small boxlike devices, which can be plugged directly into a wall socket, filter the regular current in such a way as to protect the computer from these harmful power aberrations.

The protectors, in their simplest, but still effective forms, are not expensive—only about $25 at most computer stores. It's unfortunate that computer manufacturers don't actually package one with the basic unit the new owner takes home, or build one into the power supplies of the computer itself.

Defeat dust, the silent enemy

While household dust is not as serious a threat as power variations, it, too, can cause problems with computer systems. Over a period of time, dust buildup in the keyboard or along internal circuits can produce contact failures or other problems.

The defense against dust takes two forms, both of which are simple and inexpensive. When the computer is not in use, it should be kept covered against settling dust. If a store-bought cover isn't available, you can use a pillow case, towel or piece of plastic. Be sure that the keyboard, disk drive openings and open ventilation grills are under the protective tent.

Every few months use an inexpensive can of compressed air to blow away dust from the spaces around the keys. Point the tiny nozzle into these cracks while depressing the cap to release pressured air. Loose dust will be blown out, often in surprising quantities. Use a soft, clean rag, very slightly dampened, to wipe away the residue from the nearby surfaces. (You can use a low-powered hand vacuum cleaner with a brush-nozzle attachment instead of the compressed air. But don't use a so-called dust tool attached to a regular vacuum cleaner. It's too clumsy to use and may cause nicks and scratches in the process of sucking up the dust.)

Keep a clean screen

Some dust will be attracted by static charges on the monitor screen during use. Just as with a regular TV set, the screen surface will often become contaminated with a hazy film of dust and airborne grease. This should be removed periodically in order to restore screen legibility and brightness. Clean it only when the computer is turned off.

Don't use plain water. Instead, apply any of the clear, nonabrasive glass cleaning solutions available at the grocer's sparingly to a paper towel or soft, clean cloth. Then use the lightly moistened material to wipe away the film. A second pass may be necessary to eliminate all visible traces of the problem.

Keep a clean case

Use the same sort of mild, nonabrasive cleaning solution to wipe away dirt and grime from the keyboard and surrounding surfaces. First turn the power off. Never let any excess liquid run into the computer "innards." And never let this watery cleaning fluid touch any of the interior

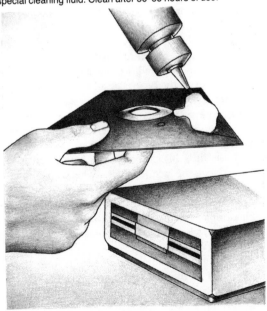

DON'T FORGET to keep your disk drive record/play heads clean. Kits like this one feature a spongy disk and special cleaning fluid. Clean after 50-60 hours of use.

YOU CAN USE any of the commercially available audio-recorder kits to clean your computer's tape recorder. Be sure you use a sponge swab that won't scratch the head.

metallic parts of a disk drive, cassette recorder or printer. This could easily cause damaging rust.

Getting inside disk and cassette drives

The disk drives are the most trouble-prone parts of a computer system. These do have moving parts that can—and do—lose critical alignments and that can—and do—wear out.

If you have not been specifically trained to work on computer disk drives, you should avoid any tool-based invasions into these rather delicate mechanisms. A broken disk unit is best repaired by an expert having both training and special apparatus.

But there are several things you can do to help disk drives give their best performance.

Keep the disk drives covered over when the computer is not actually in use to keep out dust. Keep the disk drive gates closed except when loading or unloading.

Use commercially available head cleaners periodically to rid the magnetic recording/playback heads of residues shed off the disks by the rapidly spinning surfaces. The best advice seems to be that these special gauzy disks (usually containing a special cleaning solution) should be used after every 50–60 hours or so of use. The experts say that too frequent application of these somewhat expensive contrivances is both unnecessary and uneconomical.

Computer cassette machines also require head cleaning, but far more often. Every 10 hours of use is a wise interval. You can use commercial head cleaners, although denatured alcohol dabbed on a tight gauze or sponge rubber swab (not cotton) and applied to the head structure in a gentle back-and-forth, then up-and-down motion will do just as well, and much more cheaply.

Never clean diskette heads in this "rough-and-ready" way, however. They are far too delicate to risk to the large-scale motions of a jabbing cotton swab!

What not to clean

If you own a hard-disk drive, leave all cleaning chores to the professionals. Luckily, however, these carefully encased, memory-rich media seldom require much cleaning or routine care.

A similar warning must be given about the more common floppy disks. While the disk drives do require occasional home care, the disks themselves should never be subjected to surface cleaning.

A floppy diskette that has been contaminated with any sort of foreign substance is best removed from service. Trying to run it, even after cleaning, is very apt to foul up the machine heads and lead to a sizable repair bill.

Give a little reinforcement

It's a good habit to provide extra protection to those special diskettes on which you keep very valuable records and programs. These disks receive heavy use, which puts a strain on their weakest point—the rim of the big center hole. The rim can become enlarged, losing the precise mechanical contact necessary for proper track alignment in both recording and playback modes.

Computer stores usually sell a kit to reinforce the rims of valuable disks with a little plastic ring. A special centering tool fits the new rim to the disk with exact precision. A diskette reinforced in this way is likely to give much longer active service than a conventional one. (Incidentally, very expensive diskettes often have the extra reinforcing rings added to their rims in the first place.)

Provide another kind of reinforcement

Make backup copies of valuable disks and cassettes. As a general rule, any stored files you have should be maintained in duplicate, the original and a copy. This may sound expensive and time-consuming. But when an irreplaceable disk or cassette is lost, damaged or erased, the cost of the routine "dupes" will seem altogether worthwhile.

What about the printer?

In general, printers require little user maintenance aside from changing ribbons. Even so using a compressed air canister every few weeks can prevent dust and ribbon-residue from clogging up moving mechanisms. A liquid platen cleaner—the same kind used on regular typewriters—can also help keep a computer's platen like new. And the type-face solvents available for electric typewriters are often just as effective on printer daisy wheels. Remove the daisy wheel from the printer itself—carefully following the manual's advice—and apply the chemical fluid with the little brush that comes with the solvent kit. Always be gentle: Daisy wheels are by no means indestructible.

The printing head of a dot matrix printer may need replacement from time to time. Specific instructions will be found in the manual of the particular printer involved.

Major printer adjustments, aside from those described in the printer manual, are best left to competent service personnel having special gear. It's not an amateur's task.

MANY BRANDS of disks don't have reinforced rims on the large center hole. This tool lets you apply plastic hubs to guard against rim damage and maintain precise mechanical contact for proper track alignment.

What about oiling?

Computers and oil mix no better than water and oil. And the results can be considerably more unattractive.

While there are certain mechanical peripherals that do use oil (for example, printers and disk drives), the job should always be left to factory-trained technicians. Oil has no place on keyboards, even if the keys become sticky. Oil will only intensify the problem.

If machine oil finds its way to the operating surfaces inside a disk or cassette drive, there's sure to be serious trouble, often requiring an expensive trip to the repair shop.

The best rule is: *Keep oil away from computers.*

Going inside the computer case

A computer's outer case should be opened only when absolutely necessary. There are few things an untrained user can do there to help—but lots to hurt.

If there was ever an inner sanctum for the highly trained expert, the inside of a computer is it. As a matter of fact, removing the case can even void a warranty. That's how strongly manufacturers feel about the danger. Don't be tempted to do it unless you *know positively* what you're doing. (The same warning should apply to the video monitor as well.)

It's true that at the beginning of the microcomputer age, just a few short years ago, electronic hobbyists regarded the logic boards inside their computers as the special province of tinkerers. They didn't hesitate to look inside and even change things around. It was truly an age of experimentation. But nowadays, computer designers have created extremely complex electronic architectures inside the sealed case. A mere hobbyist is apt to take the computer's life into his or her hands by tinkering with the sophisticated internal circuitry. Even the advanced pros enter those precincts with caution!

Those amateurs who ignore this advice should at least harken to the urgent plea of the experts: *Never go inside a computer or monitor unless the electric power is OFF!* To do so can be fatal—to computer or to user!

Computer workstation

■ AS IMPORTANT as your computer and its peripherals is a desk to put it on that is functional, attractive, inexpensive and ergonomically correct—that is, designed to put the components in the proper positions for the most comfortable use. This computer workstation can be custom-tailored to your own requirements. It's easy to build, extremely versatile and will fit comfortably in almost any home office. It can even be built in sections and added to as your needs grow.

The workstation deliberately does not look high-tech so it can blend in with your home decor. Yet this home computer center is more advanced than most office workstations. It's filled with clever features, most of which are hidden from view.

The workstation shown here was built for an Apple IIe, with a single disk drive and optional joystick. In addition to Apple's black and white monitor, a color monitor was added for games and graphics. The printer is a Gemini 15. The dimensions of the workstation modules were determined by the size of these components plus basic ergonomic measurements.

Building the workstation

The workstation is easy to build. The sides of each unit are higher than the tops so you have only a simple butt joint to make. There are no curves to cut, and all of the major surfaces—the

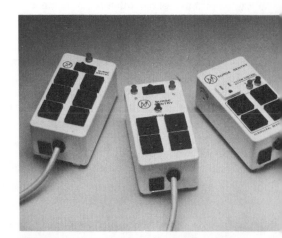

SURGE PROTECTORS are available that slip under the monitor, putting power control for your computer and peripherals within easy reach.

tops, sides and backs—are formed from a single piece. All hardware is available at any hardware store.

The workstation is built of oak cabinet–grade plywood with plastic laminate tops. You could use solid hardwood or solid pine throughout, but costs will mount. Painted plywood would make a functional substitute. Don't use an oil finish for surfaces that may come in contact with floppy disks. Laminate is best, though polyurethane varnish or paint are okay.

With the ergonomic guidelines, you'll end up with furniture that's as advanced as the computer it holds.

The computer module

The heart of the workstation is the terminal desk. If your space or funds are limited, you can build just this unit to support your keyboard, disk drives and monitor. If you have just one monitor, you can make your desk a bit narrower, although a desk for a single monitor still should be about 30 in. wide.

Otherwise, all the dimensions of the terminal desk are tailored to suit the computer. You'll need to measure your system components before modifying these plans. The most important dimensions are the height of the monitor and the distance between your eyes and the screen.

MATERIALS LIST
COMPUTER MODULE

Key	No.	Size and description (use)
A	2	¾ x 30 x 55½" oak veneer plywood (sides)
B	2	¾ x 25¼ x 30" oak veneer plywood (inside end panel)
C	1	¾ x 29⅝ x 39¼" particleboard (desk top)
D	2	¾ x 15 x 39¼" oak veneer plywood (top and bottom shelf)
E	1	¾ x 18⅞ x 39¼" oak veneer plywood (back)
F	1	¾ x 2 x 39¼" pine (top support)
G	1	¾ x 5 x 39¼" pine (stretcher)
H	1	¾ x 12¾ x 16¼" oak veneer plywood (divider)
I	2	¾ x 2 x 16" pine (cleats)
J	1	¾ x 3 x 10" oak veneer plywood (drawer front)
K	2	½ x 3 x 17¼" lauan mahogany plywood (drawer sides)
L	1	½ x 2¼ x 9½" lauan mahogany plywood (drawer back)
M	1	¼ x 8½ x 17" lauan mahogany plywood (drawer bottom)
N		¹⁄₁₆" oak veneer
O	1	¹⁄₁₆ x 29⅝ x 39¼" plastic laminate*
P	1 pr.	16" center drawer slide
Q	1	Brass drawer pull
R	4	Floor glide
S	1	¾ x 23 x 30 x 30" particleboard (removable shelf)
T	1	¹⁄₁₆ x 23 x 30 x 30" plastic laminate*
U	2	¾ x ¾ x 27" pine (cleats)
V	2	¼"-dia. x 1" hardwood dowel
W	6	1¼" No. 10 flathead screw

Misc.: Carpenter's glue, linseed oil, paste wax, con-

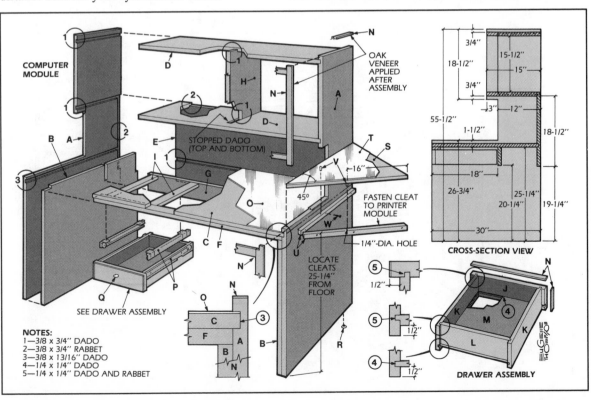

COMPUTER
MODULE

OAK
VENEER
APPLIED
AFTER
ASSEMBLY

STOPPED DADO
(TOP AND BOTTOM)

FASTEN CLEAT
TO PRINTER
MODULE

45°

16"

¼"-DIA. HOLE

LOCATE
CLEATS
25-1/4"
FROM
FLOOR

SEE DRAWER ASSEMBLY

NOTES:
1—3/8 x 3/4" DADO
2—3/8 x 3/4" RABBET
3—3/8 x 13/16" DADO
4—1/4 x 1/4" DADO
5—1/4 x 1/4" DADO AND RABBET

CROSS-SECTION VIEW

¾"
15-1/2"
18-1/2"
15"
¾"
3"
12"
55-1/2"
1-1/2"
18-1/2"
18"
26-3/4"
25-1/4"
20-1/4"
19-1/4"
30"

1/2"

DRAWER ASSEMBLY

To support the weight of two monitors it was necessary to suspend the monitor shelf from a top shelf using a central divider. If your system includes two monitors, you *must* use both the top shelf and divider. All wiring is hidden behind the back, and brought into a filtered power strip and surge protector available at most electronic or computer stores. The pencil drawer is optional or can be switched to the other side of the desk.

The printer unit

The printer console is designed to hold a Gemini 15 or similar printer. Measure your printer and modify the dimensions accordingly. The console holds the printer on a fixed shelf, accessible from both front and top through the lift-up, counterbalanced lid. An optional window lets you check print quality without opening the soundproof lid.

Beneath the printer there's room for paper storage, accessible from the front of the console. A box of continuous-feed paper fits behind the paper storage.

MATERIALS LIST
PRINTER MODULE

Key	No.	Size and description (use)
A	2	¾ x 29¾ x 30″ oak veneer plywood (sides)
B	1	¾ x 24 x 28⅛″ oak veneer plywood (back)
C	1	¾ x 23 x 29⅝″ oak veneer plywood (lid top)
D	1	¾ x 6⅝ x 23″ oak veneer plywood (lid front)
E	1	¾ x 24 x 29⅝″ oak veneer plywood (bottom)
F	1	¾ x 3⅜ x 24″ oak veneer plywood (kick)
G	1	¾ x 13⅜ x 24″ oak veneer plywood (shelf)
H	1	¾ x 6 x 24″ oak veneer plywood (shelf face)
I	1	¾ x 13 x 23″ oak veneer plywood (adjustable shelf)
J	2	¾ x 11⅜ x 18¼″ oak veneer plywood (doors)
K	2	¾ x ¾ x 5¾″ pine (lid stop)
L1	1	¼ x 1¼ x 23¼″ pine (shelf lip)
L2	1	¼ x 1¼ x 23″ pine (shelf lip)
M1	2	3/16 x ⅝ x 11½″ pine (cleats)
M2	2	3/16 x ⅝ x 3⅛″ pine (cleats)
N	1	⅛ x 3½ x 11½ glass
O	1	1/16 x 23⅛ x 30 1/16″ plastic laminate
P		1/16″ oak veneer
Q	1	1½ x 23″ brass continuous hinge
R	2 pr.	1¾ x 2″ brass butt hinge
S	3	Brass drawer pull
T	2	Magnetic catch
U	4	Shelf clip
V	4	Floor glide
W	1	13 x 23¼″ vibration pad
X	4	1¼″ No. 10 flathead brass screws
Y	1	10″ lid support

Misc.: Carpenter's glue, linseed oil, paste wax, contact cement

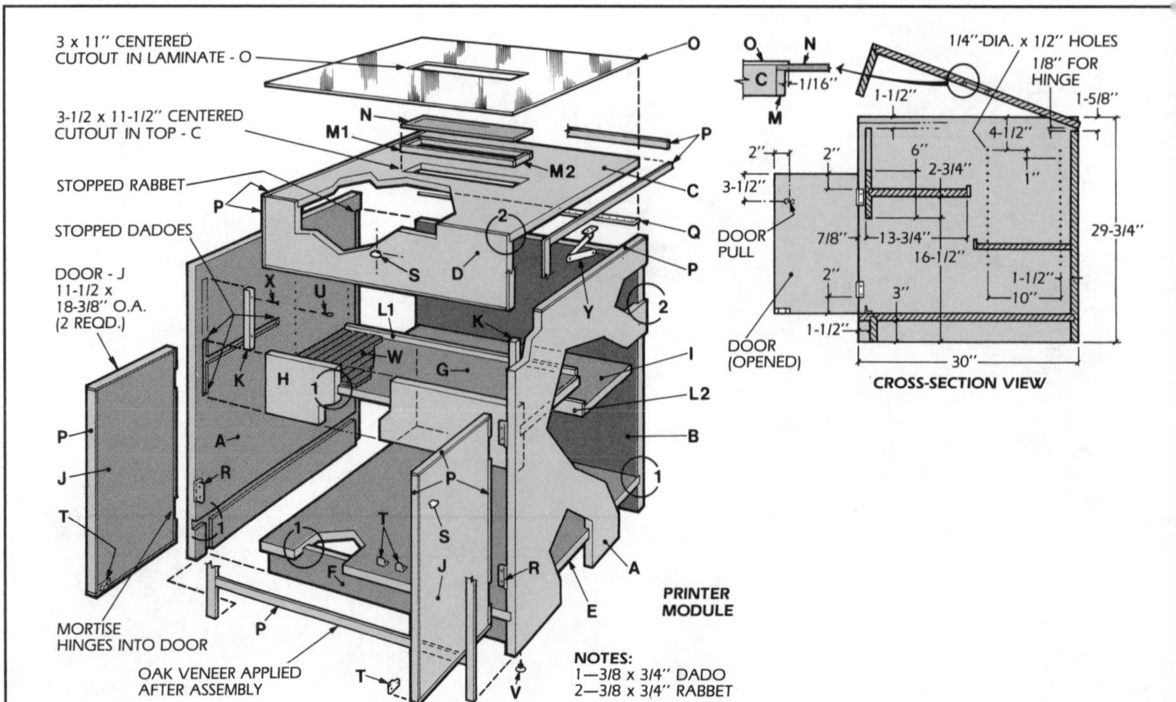

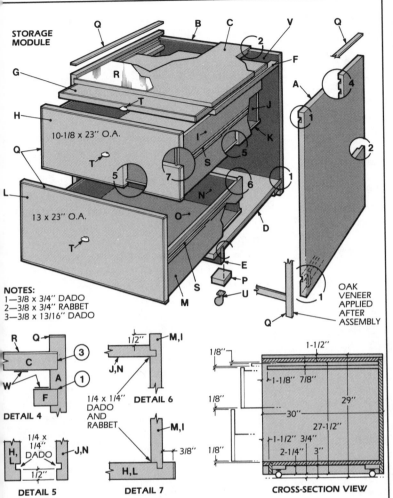

STORAGE MODULE

10-1/8 x 23" O.A.

13 x 23" O.A.

NOTES:
1—3/8 x 3/4" DADO
2—3/8 x 3/4" RABBET
3—3/8 x 13/16" DADO

OAK VENEER APPLIED AFTER ASSEMBLY

DETAIL 4

1/4 x 1/4" DADO AND RABBET

DETAIL 6

1/4 x 1/4" DADO

DETAIL 5

DETAIL 7

CROSS-SECTION VIEW

Key	No.	Size and description (use)
MATERIALS LIST		
STORAGE MODULE		
A	2	¾ x 29 x 30" oak veneer plywood (sides)
B	1	¾ x 24 x 27⅞" particleboard (back)
C	1	¾ x 24 x 30" particleboard (top)
D	1	¾ x 24 x 29⅝" particleboard (bottom)
E	1	¾ x 2⅝ x 24" oak veneer plywood (kick)
F	2	¾ x 1⅛ x 28⅛" pine (shelf support)
G	1	¾ x 23 x 29" oak veneer plywood (pull-out shelf)
UPPER DRAWER		
H	1	¾ x 10 x 23" oak veneer plywood (front)
I	2	½ x 9¼ x 19" lauan mahogany plywood (sides)
J	1	½ x 8½ x 21¾" lauan mahogany plywood (back)
K	1	¼ x 18½ x 21¾" lauan mahogany plywood (bottom)
LOWER DRAWER		
L	1	¾ x 12⅞ x 23" lauan mahogany plywood (front)
M	2	½ x 6¾ x 19" lauan mahogany plywood (sides)
N	1	½ x 6 x 21¾" lauan mahogany plywood (back)
O	1	¼ x 18½ x 21¾" lauan mahogany plywood (bottom)
P	4	¾ x 3½ x 3½" plywood (mounting blocks)
Q		¹⁄₁₆" oak veneer
R		¹⁄₁₆ x 24 x 30" plastic laminate
S	2 pr.	18" full extension drawer slide
T	3	Brass drawer pulls
U	4	Casters
V	2	¾" No. 8 roundhead screw (adjusting screw)

Misc.: Carpenter's glue, linseed oil, paste wax, contact cement

Output paper falls onto a shelf behind the printer. This can be adjusted for the proper fall, has a lip to get the paper stack started and can be removed for access to the paper box. If you print single sheets rather than continuous-feed paper, the output paper shelf can be set in its highest position and used for storing input sheets.

The printer console can be positioned next to the terminal desk along the same wall, turned 90° to make an L, or as shown, on a 30° angle. The gap is filled with a removable triangular shelf matched to the terminal desk for height. If you select the L, a square filler piece adds extra space that is perfect for holding a telephone or disk-storage carousel.

Storage cabinet

The rolling storage cabinet matches the printer console. It can be pushed back against the wall or

STORAGE MODULE holds everything from manuals to disk cases.

rolled forward next to you. The bottom drawer is sized to hold two rows of standard ring binders, and the drawer sides are cut down so you can read the spines of the notebooks easily. The top drawer holds disk-storage boxes—three rows of 5¼-in. disks or two rows of 8-in. disks.

Tucked beneath the top is a pull-out writing surface. And behind the drawers is a hidden compartment accessible only by removing the drawers. It's perfect for a small safe or fireproof storage box for valuable papers. The casters are hidden behind the recessed kick panel.

How to think ergonomically

The whole point of a custom-designed workstation is to ensure maximum comfort. You may have to modify the dimensions to accommodate your equipment and yourself. These guidelines will help.

Start with your chair. It should have an adjust-

BACKREST
SCREEN
18-20"
KEYS JUST ABOVE ELBOW HEIGHT
90°
ADJUSTABLE HEIGHT

able seat, lumbar (lower back) support and backrest. Armrests should be removable, if you have them at all. Adjust the chair so that when you sit erect, with feet flat on the floor, your thighs are parallel to the floor.

The home row keys of the keyboard should be at or just above your elbow height when you're seated properly. Usually, this means from 28 to 31 in. from the floor.

Remember to leave enough room for your thighs under the desk top. About 95 percent of American men require 25¼ in. from the floor to the bottom of the desk top for leg clearance, and 25 in. generally is considered the minimum. The angle between your upper and lower arms should be 90°, through a range of 80° to 120° up or down.

The position of the monitor is especially critical if you expect to avoid eyestrain. The top of the screen should be at or just below the horizontal plane of your eyes when you're sitting erect. The center of the screen should be 10° to 20° below the horizontal plane of your eye height, and the bottom of the screen within 40°.

Perhaps the most important of all, the distance between your eyes and the monitor should be 18 to 20 in. The screen should *never* be more than 27 in. from your eyes. Printed text should be the same distance from your eyes as the screen.

The biggest cause of eyestrain is glare from the monitor screen. You can minimize this by keeping your work area at a low ambient light level—between 500 and 700 lux—using indirect lighting. For printed material, use adjustable spot lighting.

Ideally, your work area should be 68° to 72° F and 30 to 40 percent humidity. Bright colors are distracting. Neutral colors should be used, especially for the desk top. Even under the best conditions, working at a computer for six hours without a break is about the limit. Otherwise, you risk eyestrain.

Cast your own patio slabs

■ DON'T MAKE A BIG DEAL out of pouring a concrete patio pad. Instead, do the work in easy steps which you can spread over a number of days.

The hard way is to prepare the patio area, build the forms, and then order a truckload of ready-mix concrete. When the truck arrives at your curb, you have to have a crew ready with wheelbarrows to haul the whole load to the patio. You have to fill the forms, top them off, and finish them—now. There isn't a moment to lose.

The easy way is to set up your forms as shown here—a network of redwood form boards designed to be a part of the final pad. Once you have these forms set up, you then can use pre-bagged concrete mixes. You can mix enough concrete to finish a couple of the squares today, and then relax instead of breaking your back. Tomorrow you can do a few more squares at a leisurely pace. If you keep at it, all the concrete will be laid by the end of the week.

The first step in casting this patio is to stake out the pad area. Plan to make the pad 2 in. thick, on top of a base of sand from 2 to 4 in. thick. Excavate to the proper depth, then build the forms out of redwood. The size of the form boards depends on your design. You can use 1 x

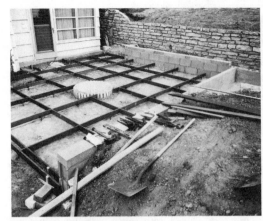

REDWOOD BOARDS are used to build a crosshatch of form boards. The boards stay in place and become a part of the final patio design.

DRY SAND is used as a base for the concrete. Use at least 2 in. of sand. Place the sand in the forms, then level it, leaving 2 in. for the concrete.

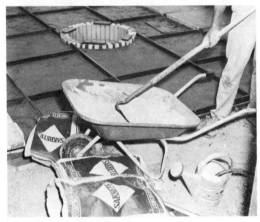

USE PRE-BAGGED concrete mix, which you can mix, following the directions on the bag, in a wheelbarrow. Be sure to mix thoroughly.

FILL EACH SQUARE, then strike the concrete level with a board. Finally, use a wooden float, as shown here, to finish the square.

4- or 2 x 4-in. boards. Use stakes to hold the boards in place.

With the boards in place, lay in the sand base and level it, allowing space for a 2-in. concrete pad. Note that the concrete used in a 2-in. pad should have a 4000-psi strength rating. Check the bag for a strength rating. Good mixes such as Sakrete have it. Poorer ones offer only 2000-psi ratings, and should be poured to a depth of 4 in.

Once the forms are in place, mix enough concrete to finish a couple of pads at a time. Follow the instructions on the bag and mix thoroughly.

Fill the form to the top of the form boards and use a long board as a striker to level the concrete. Then float the finish, using a wooden cement float, by running the float back and forth across the surface. When water appears on the surface, stop. The job is finished.

Allow the concrete to begin to set, then use an edger (your hardware store has them) to round off the edge along the line where the concrete meets the form boards.

Curing the new patio pads is important. The concrete should be kept damp for at least two days and preferably four or five. Cover each pad after finishing with a plastic sheet, and spray the surface with water before covering. In hot weather especially, lift the cover a couple of times a day during the curing to spray again. The slower and more complete the cure, the stronger the pads will be.

After all of the pads have been cured, you can sharpen the appearance of the new patio by cleaning up the redwood boards. Go over them with a wire brush to get rid of any cement or water stains.

Concrete slabs—pour them yourself

■ MAKE NO MISTAKE about it, plenty of hard work is involved in pouring concrete yourself. But there is an immediate reward—one you can see in your wallet. However, if you don't do the job right, you may have to live with a cracked or heaving slab or drainage problems—that could require breaking up the slab into rubble and starting over. Use the professional know-how on these pages and your savings will be permanent.

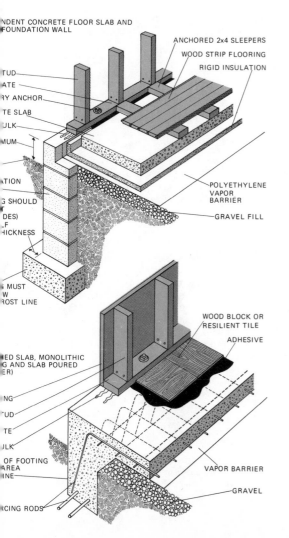

NDENT CONCRETE FLOOR SLAB AND
FOUNDATION WALL

ANCHORED 2x4 SLEEPERS

WOOD STRIP FLOORING

RIGID INSULATION

TUD

ATE

RY ANCHOR

TE SLAB

ULK

MUM

TION

G SHOULD

DES)
F
HICKNESS

POLYETHYLENE
VAPOR
BARRIER

GRAVEL FILL

MUST
W
ROST LINE

WOOD BLOCK OR
RESILIENT TILE

ADHESIVE

ED SLAB, MONOLITHIC
G AND SLAB POURED
ER)

NG

UD

TE

JLK

OF FOOTING
AREA
INE

VAPOR BARRIER

GRAVEL

CING RODS

Typical slab contruction

Thickened-edge, monolithic slab-and-footing combinations are recommended for patios, with or without a roof structure or bearing wall above. Independent footings, foundation walls and slabs are the better way when an enclosed structure will be built over the slab; this allows for placing of perimeter insulation and vapor barrier in stages between pours. The bottom of the footing always must be below the area frost line.

Several basic construction rules should be adhered to throughout any job: First, never refill the excavation or trench with dirt if you've dug too deep—pour extra concrete instead. Second, most footings should be a minimum of 12 in. deep, and twice the width of the foundation-wall thickness. For example, for a wall built of 8-in. block, footings should be 16 in. wide, projecting 4 in. to either side of the wall. Third, if the soil is of a low load-bearing capacity, you may find it will be necessary to construct wider and reinforced footings.

"Load bearing capacity" refers to all the weight that will be imposed on each lineal foot of perimeter area (footing area) by the structure above, the live weight it will carry and the snow load on the roof. As all soil has a maximum bearing capacity in tons per sq. ft., it is an important factor in footing design. Imagine standing on a 1-ft.-square piece of plywood on dry beach sand, and then trying the same thing in a marsh—the plywood has to be a lot bigger or you'll sink. Your local building department can provide general information on soil load-bearing capacity in your area. If any question remains about your property in particular, you can have a qualified engineer (P.E.) check it for you.

For small jobs you'll find it most economical to buy the sand, aggregate (gravel) and cement and mix them yourself—by hand or with a rented cement mixer. Or you can use a commercially prepared mix sold by the bag. But for the big jobs—a driveway, for example—your best bet is to buy ready-mixed concrete.

The best time to pour is when the temperature is between 40° and 85° F. Cold-weather pouring adds so many complications the homeowner should avoid it. In hot, dry weather, subgrade and forms should be dampened. If it rains on the day you've planned to place concrete, re-schedule the job. If you want to color your concrete, use mineral-oxide pigment; it's sold in several colors at most paint and hardware stores. Mix it with sand before combining ingredients. Pigment used should never be more than 10 percent, by weight, of the cement used; otherwise it will weaken the slab. Colored ready-mix concrete is available, but usually only in large quantities.

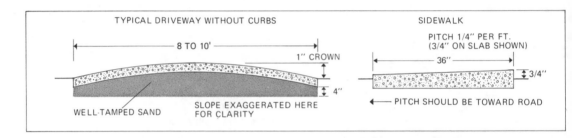

Typical slabs for driveway and sidewalk

Each slab shown above is pitched for positive water runoff. A typical driveway (left), 8 to 10 ft. wide, has a 1-in. crown at the center and a pitch of ¼ in. per foot along its length to divert rainwater. A sidewalk from edge to edge is also pitched ¼ in. per foot (right) — its low side should drain toward the street, not onto your property. The driveway slab thickness should be 5 in. minimum. If the driveway is going to be used for heavy loads, you should pour a 6-in. slab and use steel-mesh to act as reinforcing. The typical sidewalk slab would be 4 in. thick.

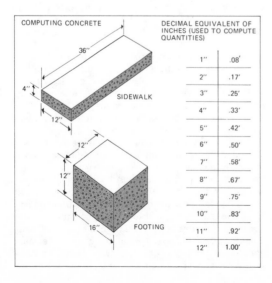

COMPUTING CONCRETE	DECIMAL EQUIVALENT OF INCHES (USED TO COMPUTE QUANTITIES)	
	1″	.08′
	2″	.17′
	3″	.25′
	4″	.33′
	5″	.42′
	6″	.50′
	7″	.58′
	8″	.67′
	9″	.75′
	10″	.83′
	11″	.92′
	12″	1.00′

Computing quantities

Ready-mix concrete is sold by the cubic yard; 1 cu. yd. is usually the minimum order. To compute the amount you will need, you must find the cubic footage of the slab to be poured, then convert this figure to cubic yards. Multiply length by width by thickness in feet, then divide by 27. Decimal equivalents of inches make the calculation easier.

Sidewalk slab, 4 x 12 x 36 in.:
$$\frac{0.33 \times 1 \times 3}{27} = 0.037 \text{ cu. yd.}$$
Section of footing, 12 x 12 x 16 in.
$$\frac{1 \times 1 \times 1.33}{27} = 0.049 \text{ cu. yd.}$$

Thus, if your run (lineal footage) of this footing were 20 ft., you would need about 1 cu. yd. of concrete.

It is good practice to add about 5 percent for waste to your estimate—roughly, 1 cu. yd for each 20.

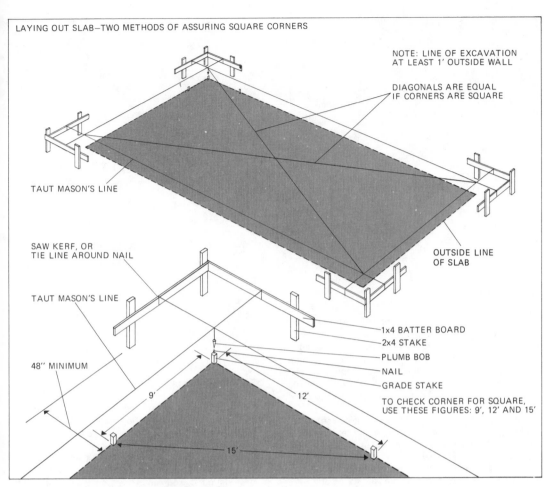

LAYING OUT SLAB—TWO METHODS OF ASSURING SQUARE CORNERS

NOTE: LINE OF EXCAVATION
AT LEAST 1' OUTSIDE WALL

DIAGONALS ARE EQUAL
IF CORNERS ARE SQUARE

TAUT MASON'S LINE

OUTSIDE LINE
OF SLAB

SAW KERF, OR
TIE LINE AROUND NAIL

TAUT MASON'S LINE

1x4 BATTER BOARD
2x4 STAKE
PLUMB BOB
NAIL
GRADE STAKE

48" MINIMUM

9'

12'

TO CHECK CORNER FOR SQUARE,
USE THESE FIGURES: 9', 12' AND 15'

15'

How to lay out a slab with square corners

To lay a slab, you must locate a grade stake accurately at each of the corners. Each way shown above will give precise, square corners if done properly. Batter boards (on firmly anchored stakes) should be leveled one to the next. Use a plumb bob, or 20d nail or larger, to set the grade nails at the corners. Fix a mason's line to saw kerfs in batter boards or use common nails so the line can be repositioned if it becomes disturbed. Be sure to allow for the form width when you are excavating. Tamp the ground thoroughly, below the footing, before you begin pouring.

Water use important when mixing and pouring concrete

Water content of concrete is extremely important. For a strong mix, water should not exceed 6 gal. per full sack (94 lb.) of cement. Use clean water only—as a rule of thumb, if you can drink it, you can use it for concrete. Add just enough to make the mix workable. Although too much water makes pouring easy it also keeps cement from adhering to the aggregate. The result of such a pour will be a weak slab.

For most homeowner jobs, a mix ratio of cement to fine aggregate (sand) to coarse aggregate (gravel) of 1, 2 and 3 is best. Ready-mix concrete may not offer you a choice of ratios, and the mix may have to be varied with the size of gravel—measured by the maximum diameter of the pieces of stone—locally available. Coarse aggregate with a maximum size of 2 in. is not recommended for slabs; 1

to 1½ in. is normal.

Mixing your own concrete, when practical, gives you greater control. For a 1:2:3 ratio, a good guideline is that the volume of sand used should be about 2/3 of the volume of coarse aggregate. For a 100-sq.-ft. slab 4 in. thick, you would need 0.64 cu. yd. of sand, 0.95 cu. yd. of gravel and 8.4 sacks of cement. You can figure on using about seven sacks of cement for each cubic yard of concrete at a 1:2:3 ratio.

Whenever possible, concrete should be poured continuously and kept practically level throughout the area being placed. Where the sides of a slab will be visible, smack the forms smartly with a hammer. This will prevent what is called a "honeycomb" appearance, caused by air bubbles, and give neat, good-looking edges.

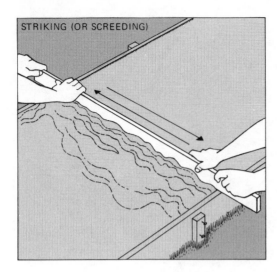

STRIKING (OR SCREEDING)

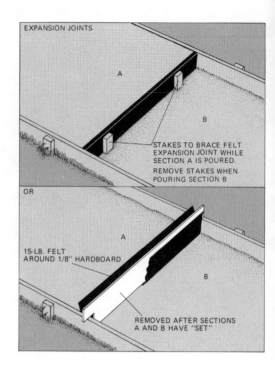

EXPANSION JOINTS

A

B

STAKES TO BRACE FELT EXPANSION JOINT WHILE SECTION A IS POURED. REMOVE STAKES WHEN POURING SECTION B

OR

A

15-LB. FELT AROUND 1/8" HARDBOARD

B

REMOVED AFTER SECTIONS A AND B HAVE "SET"

Surface finishing

After concrete is poured, it must be struck (trade terms are striking and screeding) immediately by drawing a board back and forth across the surface. Use a side-to-side sawing motion as you advance; press projecting stones (aggregate) below the surface. When concrete built up ahead of the screed makes it difficult to move, shovel the excess away. To crown a driveway, the underside of the strikeboard is cut concave.

An hour after striking off, the surface can be "floated," bringing water to the top and texturing the concrete. Work a wood float in a swirling motion, taking care not to "saucer" any spot—or it will collect puddles. For a smooth surface, follow the floating with a steel trowel, used in wide, sweeping arcs. Do not trowel until the water sheen has left the surface. Keep in mind that neither floating nor troweling should be overdone—too much water brought up will make the slab weaker. Excess troweling also brings up "fines," small particles that make the surface produce dust.

After floating and troweling (if desired) and removing separators, round off slab edges with an edger and finish cross joints with groover.

Expansion joints

Driveways should be divided into 20-ft.-long sections using felt expansion joints (top drawing). Brace the joint as shown while pouring the first section. Remove stakes when enough concrete has been poured in the second section to make the felt immovable. If sidewalks are to have separated slabs, separators should be placed at intervals of 6 ft. You can make separators of 1/8-in. tempered hardboard inserted in folded tarpaper. Place them at right angles to the slab forms, and pour concrete on both sides of each one to keep them straight. When you finish the surface, remove the hardboard but leave the tarpaper in place in the joint. Excess can be trimmed away after concrete has set. False expansion joints—for appearance—can be made with a groover after surface finishing has been done.

Curing time extends for weeks

Curing of concrete is a chemical process that continues for weeks after pouring. New concrete must be kept damp or the evaporation of water will make hydration (the combination of water with cement and aggregate) incomplete and your slab weak. Cover the surface with burlap, felt or layers of newspaper and keep this covering moist for five to seven days—at least a week in hot, dry weather. Depending on temperature and humidity levels, moisten once or twice a day.

THE EASIEST reinforcement to install is steel block mesh set right in the mortar. The ends of the mesh strips should be overlapped for greatest strength.

Concrete block laying tips

■ YOU'RE NOT A MASON, so why try to lay blocks like one? Especially when you can get better results by taking advantage of your amateur status.

A professional mason spends years mastering the skills of his trade. Once he has acquired the necessary experience, he can lay blocks quickly with a machine-like efficiency that seems almost effortless. On the first job, though, the professional method is actually much more difficult than a straightforward amateur approach.

The following professional method of laying concrete blocks is designed for an unskilled person working alone. All you need is the desire to do a good job and a few specialized tools.

The first tool to buy is a mason's trowel. This is used to pick up and place mortar. The blade is about 10 in. long and 5 in. across.

Mason's trowels come in two shapes—Boston and Philadelphia. For block laying, you'll probably prefer the Philadelphia, because its straighter edges are better for picking up straight beads of mortar.

Incidentally, professionals use the wooden trowel handle for tapping blocks into position. When amateurs try this, they usually end up spattering mortar all over. Better to resist the temptation to "do it like a pro" and position the blocks by tapping lightly with a hammer.

The hammer you use will depend on the job. A regular mason's hammer has a square head at one end and a chisel edge on the other. It's used for cutting the blocks to size, making holes or chipping the edges to special shapes. If your project doesn't include any of this type of work, you can get along very well without it.

You can't get along without an accurate level, for the whole success of the project depends upon how carefully it is leveled. As in the case of the hammer, however, it doesn't have to be a mason's level. A true mason's level is 4 ft. long, with the extra length for use as a straightedge. As

DRY LAYOUT of blocks on the footing is a good precaution. Use scraps of ⅜-in. plywood as spacers.

SMALL CONCRETE MIXER makes it possible to mix a fresh batch of mortar while you are using up the first.

BOTTOM COURSE is laid on full mortar bed which has been furrowed with a trowel point. Note the guide line.

CORNER BLOCKS are laid to interlock. These govern position of all other blocks, so level them both ways.

an amateur, you can get along fine with a good 2-ft carpenter's level.

You'll also need a jointing tool in order to produce smooth, tight mortar joints. For rounded joints, the tool to use is a ⅝-in. round bar or pipe that's curved at the ends to prevent gouging. For V-joints, use a ½-in.-sq. bar with curved ends. The ends can be used for tooling short vertical joints. A good jointing tool should be at least 22 in. long to span irregularities. The main reason for tooling mortar joints, incidentally, is to compact them and make them more weather-resistant. Just as important, though, is the fact that this finishes off the joints and produces a better-looking wall.

Other useful items are a nylon mason's line (the amateur can use a strong fishline) and a pair of line blocks. The blocks hook over the ends of the wall to anchor the line.

A small concrete mixer is also highly desirable, since it produces better, more workable mortar than you can get by mixing with a hoe or shovel. The 5-gal.-bucket type is ideal.

So much for the equipment. Now you're ready to plan the job. The most important thing here is to use modular dimensions, if possible. This will avoid hours of tedious cutting and fitting. Concrete blocks are made to fit 8-in. modules, so if you design the wall to fit them, using full and half blocks, you'll do yourself a favor. Draw a rough-dimensioned sketch to be sure you've got everything straight and you're ready to install the footing.

A good footing is twice as wide as the wall. It should be cast on unexcavated earth, not on backfill. The bottom of the footing must be below the frost line in your area and at least 12 in. deep.

Build your footing of quality concrete containing six bags of portland cement per cubic yard and not more than six gallons of water per bag of cement. Ready-mix can be ordered to these specs. If the job is small, use packaged concrete mix. Don't overwater. Place it stiff.

Strike off the footing level to the proper grade. Floating it once will make the surface as smooth as you need it. Cover with wet soil or sand and let the footing cure for six days. Then clean off all of

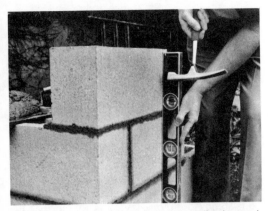

LONG FACE of each corner block must be lined up and plumb with the blocks below. Tap lightly into place.

CHECK THE HEIGHT by measuring from the footing to top of corner. If block has settled, remove and re-lay.

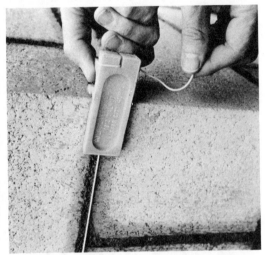

LINE BLOCK holds line flush with top of corner. Move to the next course when the blocks will stand pull.

GOOD MORTAR BOARD is an 18-in square piece of plywood. Support it on a pair of upended block legs.

RIBBONS OF MORTAR on ends of each intermediate block fill vertical joints. For best bond, slap them on.

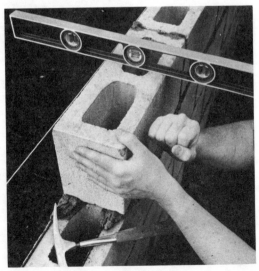

INTERMEDIATE BLOCKS should be laid to align with the guide line and leveled across to square them.

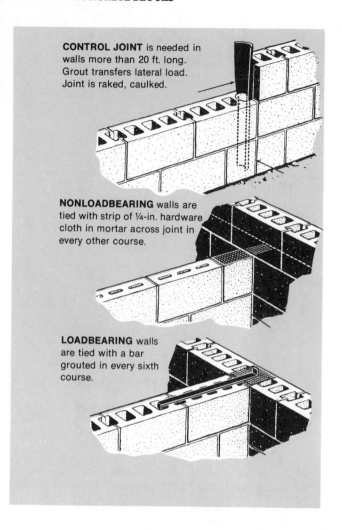

CONTROL JOINT is needed in walls more than 20 ft. long. Grout transfers lateral load. Joint is raked, caulked.

NONLOADBEARING walls are tied with strip of ¼-in. hardware cloth in mortar across joint in every other course.

LOADBEARING walls are tied with a bar grouted in every sixth course.

the sand or soil and you're all set to start laying block.

The strength of your wall will depend largely on the strength of the mortar. Also important is the "bond" of the mortar—how tightly it holds to the blocks once it has set. Your best bet is to buy a packaged mortar mix (Sakrete, for instance).

Mortar should be mixed as wet as you can get it and still have it workable. Workable mortar is buttery, yet sticky. It clings to the trowel, even holds to vertical end-joint surfaces.

A good way to judge if your mortar is the right consistency for block-laying is to see that the blocks hold to the right height while you're laying them. If they sink, add more mix to dry out the mortar. If they have to be pounded down, add more water to the mortar and re-mix. It's important to measure everything, though, so you will be sure of getting the proper mix next time.

If you have to mix the mortar by hand, spread the dry materials on a flat concrete surface or in a mortar box and add about three quarters of the water. Mix these with a hoe until the mortar is uniformly damp, then add the remaining water a little at a time while you continue mixing. Let batch stand for five minutes. Before use, remix the mortar thoroughly without adding water. Mortar not used within 2½ hours should be discarded. Within that time you can mix in more water with the trowel.

The procedure to follow when laying the

TO LAY LAST block in each course, butter the ends with mortar and lower it carefully down into the slot.

SLICE OFF MORTAR along joints of newly laid blocks without smearing. It may be remixed and used again.

TO KEEP mortar fresh, slice through it occasionally with the trowel and add more water if it is necessary.

TOOL JOINTS when mortar is thumbprint-hard by working the jointing tool back and forth along each joint.

blocks is detailed in the accompanying photos. However, one thing that can't be overstressed is the importance of control joints in any block wall more than 20 ft. long. As shown in the drawing a control joint is a continuous vertical joint from top to bottom which lets the wall change dimension slightly without cracking.

You can use either special control-joint blocks or regular blocks with provision for transferring lateral loads across the joint, as shown in the drawing. Lay up the joint with mortar. Then,

before the mortar gets too hard, rake it out to a depth of ¾ in. and fill the joint with an elastic caulking. Be sure to follow the caulking manufacturer's recommendations about priming the surface.

One final precaution: Whatever your project happens to be, make sure you check local building codes before you begin construction. Besides, your building officials are familiar with local conditions, and they often can help you get off to a good start.

ANCHOR BOLTS or other fixtures can be installed in the wall by grouting. Just place a piece of mesh across the core beneath to prevent grout from dropping to the bottom of the wall, then fill the core with concrete or mortar and set the bolt in this. To avoid the possibility of the bolt working loose, it should either have a large head or be bent to a right angle. Use ½-in. bolts for most such applications.

TO REINFORCE WALL laterally, use strips of steel block mesh, below left. For vertical reinforcement, cast reinforcing bars with bent ends into the footing and grout cores around bars as in center and lower right photos.

TOOL VERTICAL joints with end of jointing tool. Remove burrs by rubbing across joint with a wire brush.

MORTAR DEPOSITS on face of wall can be rubbed away with a piece of broken block after mortar hardens.

A thumbnail guide to concrete blocks

The workhorse of concrete blocks is the standard 8x8x16-in. block, commonly known as an 8-in block because it makes a wall 8 in. wide. You can also buy 6-in. block, which is primarily for nonloadbearing walls, and 4-in block for even slimmer nonloadbearing walls. For big jobs, like foundations and heavy retaining walls, there are 10 and 12-in blocks.

Block measurements always describe the area a block will take up when laid in the wall. Actually, the block measures ⅜ in. less on a side to allow for a ⅜ in. mortar joint. To estimate the number of blocks required for a job, figure the wall area in square feet, subtract the area of openings and multiply by 1¹⁄₉. For example, a 90-sq.-ft wall would require 100 blocks. Half blocks used at ends and corners are counted as halves, not whole units.

Most blocks have two or three cores. The two-core type, which offers somewhat better insulating qualities, is popular in the West. Both are available in standard and lightweight types, the latter containing cinders, shale or slag for aggregates. A standard block weighs from 40 to 50 lbs., a lightweight only 25 to 30 lbs.

Many blockmakers are doing away with special corner blocks, and are making all their structural blocks with square ends.

Among the glamour types are: split block (made by breaking an oversize block into two pieces so the resulting faces resemble rough stonemasonry); slump block (like adobe brick in appearance); grille or screen block (for garden walls) and sculptured block (to create a three-dimensional effect). Like all blocks, they can be painted with latex or portland-cement paint. Some makers even sell blocks ready-colored with mortar to match.

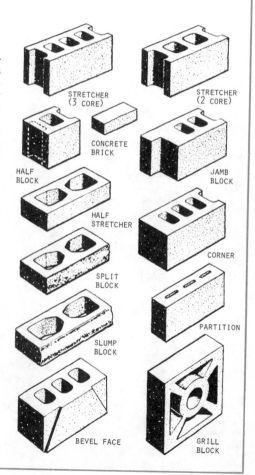

STRETCHER (3 CORE)

STRETCHER (2 CORE)

CONCRETE BRICK

HALF BLOCK

JAMB BLOCK

HALF STRETCHER

CORNER

SPLIT BLOCK

PARTITION

SLUMP BLOCK

BEVEL FACE

GRILL BLOCK

Cooling system maintenance

■ WHAT GOES THROUGH your mind when you see someone standing forlornly next to a car by the side of the road? The hood is up, and a plume of white smoke jets from the engine compartment.

Do you think, "I'm glad I'm not in that fix?"

Or do you think: "That *could* be me if my car's cooling system can't take the strain."

The people downed by cooling-system failure are normally those who take this important system for granted. Although the cooling system has been developed into one of the most reliable units in a car—only 25 years ago it required servicing every six months—it is *not* maintenance-free.

Today's cooling system will maintain efficiency for the life of the car, but only if it gets some basic maintenance periodically. "Periodically" is defined as once every two years.

Periodic service, detailed here, will do the following:

• It helps avoid engine freeze-ups during cold weather.

• It improves total cooling efficiency, assuring that the engine won't overheat.

• It helps prevent corrosion and sludge build-up in the cooling system and engine, which leads to expensive repairs.

• It allows the engine to operate within its most efficient temperature range, which provides the most effective and economical operation.

The sensible maintenance program outlined here is designed to let you avoid unnecessary work while still providing the cooling system with the conditioning it needs to remain viable. Keep in mind that this program is *preventive* maintenance—that is, maintenance which is done to help avert a breakdown. We are not discussing what has to be done if a cooling-system failure occurs—specifically, overheating. Our purpose is to avoid failure.

The sensible cooling-system maintenance program we outline here consists of seven parts, as follows:

• Checking radiator hoses.
• Checking drive belts.
• Cleaning radiator fins.
• Checking the integrity of the radiator pressure cap.
• Checking the thermostat.
• Cleaning the system.
• Filling the system with a high quality coolant which contains rust inhibitor.

Let's discuss each.

Hose examination

Examine top and bottom radiator hoses, and two heater hoses. Squeeze each hose over its *entire* length. If the hose feels spongy or exhibits cracks, replace the part. Failure of hoses is the dominant cooling system malfunction leading to roadside breakdowns.

While at it, look for corrosion or rust-colored stains around hose clamps. These signify a coolant leak. If hose clamps are the screw-tightening rather than vise type, tighten clamps and clean off deposits. If the leak reappears or clamps cannot be tightened, the hose or clamp has weakened. Both should be replaced.

The correct way to remove the old hose is the way you find easiest—cutting it off if necessary. Clean connecting surfaces thoroughly with a wire brush.

Coat connections with water-resistant sealing compound. Place new clamps on the ends of the hose, and install the new hose all the way on connections. If the ends of the hose are stiff and aren't easily manipulated, soak them in hot water for a minute or so before connecting them. Slide clamps into position. Tighten.

Be sure to locate clamps at least ⅛ inch from the ends of the hose. If they are placed at the ends, the hose may bulge behind them. That can lead to premature hose failure.

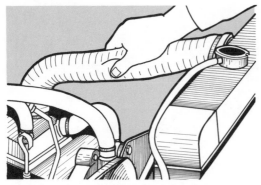

THE "FEEL" of a radiator hose will tell you if it has rotted, gotten mushy, and is due for replacement. Retire any that show cracks under pressure, too.

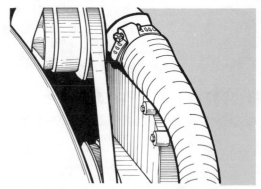

YOU'LL FEEL a spring in the lower radiator hose. If it doesn't feel tense, replace the hose. Check the drive belt's condition at the same time.

Don't discount the importance of examining heater hoses. They are part of the cooling system. Coolant flows through them just as it does through radiator hoses. If a heater hose fails, you will lose coolant and overheating will result—just as quickly as when radiator hoses fail.

Checking drive belts

If the drive belt that runs the water pump and cooling fan is damaged or not adjusted properly, cooling will be curtailed. Further, the power steering, alternator and air conditioning depend on belts.

Examine belts for cracks, frayed spots and glaze on the underside. Glaze on the belt or on the pulley will cause slipping. Belt damage of any kind is cause for its immediate replacement.

Whether the old belt is adequate or a new belt is installed, correct adjustment is necessary. A belt that is adjusted too tight will put strain on water pump, fan pulley, and alternator components, causing early failure. One that isn't tight enough can't drive components efficiently.

The most effective way of testing belt tension is with a professional drive-belt tension gauge,

which you can purchase at an automotive supply store. Hook the tool's tang on the belt and press down on the knob until resistance is met. Read the gauge and compare it to manufacturer specification in the service manual. Adjust the belt accordingly.

Without a gauge, you can judge tension by laying a straight-edge between the pulleys and pressing a ruler down on the belt at the midway point. The deflection shouldn't exceed ½ inch.

Newer cars often have a fan clutch that disengages when the engine needs less cooling. The clutch is easy to check. With the engine cold, start the car and let it warm up. As temperature increases, the clutch should engage. With no increase in engine speed, you should see the fan speed up abruptly—often with a distinct click. Otherwise the clutch probably needs repair.

Cleaning radiator fins

In the two years since your last maintenance work, lots of trash—bugs, leaves, and dirt—may have built up around the fins. It can handicap the system seriously. Clean it out with air pressure or a long-handled, soft-bristled brush.

HOSE CLAMPS should be at least ⅛ inch from the hose end and the hose seated firmly in place.

FOR EXACT drive-belt tension, a gauge is the only reliable guide. Anything else is second best.

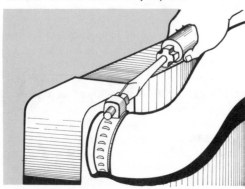

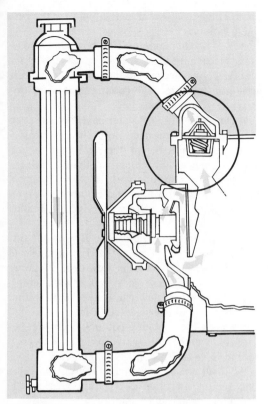

THERMOSTAT (circled) stops or permits coolant circulation according to the engine's need for cooling. Special fan clutches on newer cars have a similar role.

If you have compressed air, aim it from the side instead of directly at the fragile fins. The brush is slower, but safer. If dirt is caked on, you may need to wash the radiator surface.

Testing the radiator pressure cap

Your radiator cap is designed to let go only after coolant reaches a preselected pressure. This function is important. A modern engine

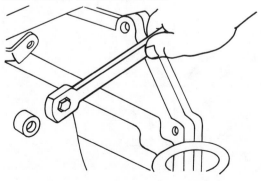

TO DRAIN ALL the coolant, remove drain plugs in the block. This one was difficult to find.

runs best with coolant under pressure. That keeps it from boiling at running temperatures above 200° F. So long as it remains liquid, the coolant keeps circulating as it should.

Under 15 pounds of pressure, the boiling point of a typical ethylene glycol mix is raised about 40° F. If it would normally boil at 225° F., a 15-pound cap prevents its boiling until about 265° F. Thus it can keep transferring excess heat from the block to the radiator where it can be rejected to the atmosphere.

Caps are checked with a cooling-system pressure tester—standard equipment at most service stations. The charge is usually nominal.

Checking the thermostat

The thermostat is another element to check. Its function: It opens to allow circulation to start only when the engine has reached running temperature.

Sooner or later, thermostats fail. Since the cooling system has to be drained for cleaning anyway, this is the time to check the thermostat, too.

Follow these steps:

1. Make sure the engine is cold. Remove the radiator pressure cap.

2. Set the heater control to ON and open the drain cock at the base of the radiator. Let old coolant drain.

3. To ensure complete draining, remove engine drain plugs. V8s usually have two, sixes and fours, one.

4. After draining, close the cock and reinsert the plugs securely.

5. Remove the thermostat bolts and move the housing aside.

6. Remove and discard the old gasket. And if, in that cold engine, the thermostat wasn't closed, discard it, too.

7. Note the thermostat's temperature rating marked on the housing.

8. Hang the thermostat from a wire in water in a heat-resistant-glass pot (glass, so you can see inside). Add a thermometer and put the pot on the stove.

9. The thermostat valve should open wide before it is 15° above its rating. If it isn't, replace the thermostat.

10. Wire-brush the mating surfaces of the thermostat housing and the engine thoroughly.

11. Reinsert the thermostat, making sure the bolt holes line up.

12. Put a *new* gasket in place, reattach the thermostat housing, and tighten the housing bolts.

Cleaning the system

If you clean the cooling system with a commercially available fast-flush chemical every two years, you probably won't ever have to have it back-flushed. Back-flushing is pressure-cleaning and requires special equipment. Follow mixing instructions printed on the package.

Occasionally increase engine speed by pressing the accelerator pedal slowly about halfway to the floor. This allows more forceful circulation that will dislodge scale.

At the end of the prescribed time, drain the system by opening the drain cock and removing the drain plugs. The heater should have been kept *on*. Do *not* remove the radiator pressure cap.

But never add cold water or coolant to a hot engine. The block may crack.

Adding antifreeze

When the discharge from the drain cock looks clear, finish draining. Close the drain cock and drain plugs and let the engine cool down. Then add a reliable brand of ethylene glycol to the cooling system.

Confusing questions are sometimes raised about ethylene glycol. Let's summarize the pertinent points:

• You needn't add anything but water to ethylene glycol antifreeze. A good brand already includes all the needed additives, including rust inhibitor, to protect the cooling system for two years.

• Don't use straight water as a coolant, even in areas where you need no antifreeze protection. You'll miss the protective additives you should have. And remember that a modern engine—especially one with air conditioning—may often run at a temperature above water's 212° boiling point. Ethylene glycol's boiling point is still higher.

• The proportion of ethylene glycol your system needs depends on how cold your area will get. Instructions are on the antifreeze container (you'll have to know your system's capacity). Drain the system down to leave ample room, then add the antifreeze called for.

• Check the coolant's potency each year before cold weather. Use a hydrometer; it's a good tool to have and needn't be expensive.

All in all, this maintenance program may take only about an hour every two years—little enough considering its importance.

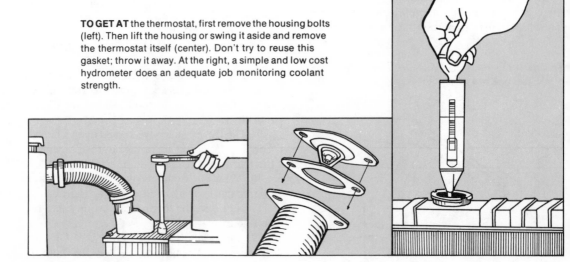

TO GET AT the thermostat, first remove the housing bolts (left). Then lift the housing or swing it aside and remove the thermostat itself (center). Don't try to reuse this gasket; throw it away. At the right, a simple and low cost hydrometer does an adequate job monitoring coolant strength.

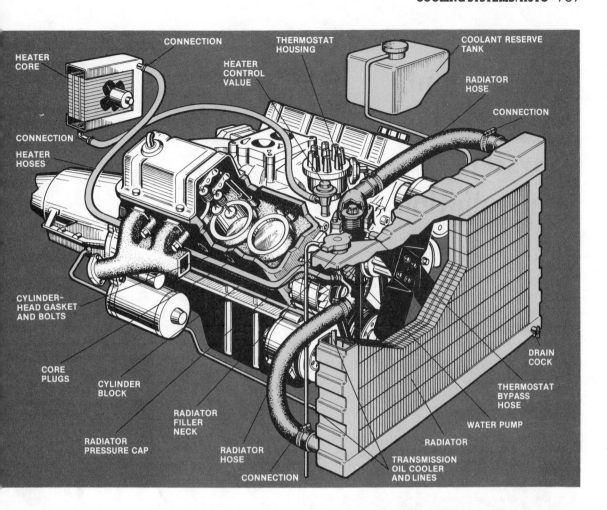

HEATER CORE

CONNECTION

THERMOSTAT HOUSING

COOLANT RESERVE TANK

HEATER CONTROL VALUE

RADIATOR HOSE

CONNECTION

CONNECTION

HEATER HOSES

CYLINDER-HEAD GASKET AND BOLTS

DRAIN COCK

CORE PLUGS

CYLINDER BLOCK

THERMOSTAT BYPASS HOSE

RADIATOR FILLER NECK

WATER PUMP

RADIATOR PRESSURE CAP

RADIATOR HOSE

RADIATOR

CONNECTION

TRANSMISSION OIL COOLER AND LINES

CAUSE	CORRECTION
...m loses coolant.	Coolant loss is a result of several factors, summarized below.
...quate ethylene ...coolant mixture.	Ethylene glycol protects engine against cold weather, also corrosion leading to curtailment of coolant flow, overheating.
	Check solution with hydrometer. Protection between −35°F. and −45°F. is considered normal.
...m loses pressure.	Test radiator-pressure cap; Check loose hose connections.
...ucted radiator.	Clean bugs, debris from fins.
...tor tubes blocked by	If flushing doesn't work, have radiator shop treat radiator chemically.
...g-system passages ...d by scale.	Flush system; add fresh coolant.
...drive belt.	Tighten.
...ative thermal control ...oupling fan.	Repair.
...ged water pump.	Repair.
...radiator hose ...ses due to weak ...al spring.	Replace hose.
...ive thermostat ...n closed position.	Replace thermostat
...ect ignition timing.	Set timing to spec; test vacuum advance for functioning.

Restricted exhaust system. — See that muffler, exhaust system pipes haven't collapsed.

Areas of coolant loss
Check the following areas when coolant is being lost:

Areas of leakage	Corrective action
☐ Radiator.	Try sealer if leak is small, repair or replace radiator if leak is large.
☐ Radiator drain cock.	Tighten if loose; replace if defective.
☐ Transmission-oil cooler lines	Tighten connections.
☐ Coolant reserve tank and hose.	Repair or replace tank; replace hose.
☐ Hoses (radiator and heater), connections.	Tighten if loose; replace if defective.
☐ Water-pump seal.	Repair.
☐ Water-pump gasket.	Replace.
☐ Radiator pressure cap.	Tighten if loose, replace if defective.
☐ Radiator filler neck.	Reform if distorted; cut off and solder on new filler neck if repair fails.
☐ Thermostat housing gasket.	Replace.
☐ Heater core.	Repair or replace
☐ Heater-water control valve.	Replace.
☐ Cylinder-head gasket.	Replace.
☐ Cylinder-head bolts.	Tighten to specification.
☐ Cylinder-block core plugs.	Replace.
☐ Warped cylinder head or blocked surface.	Resurface.
☐ Cracked cylinder head or block.	Replace.

Engine overheating trouble-shooting

FREQUENTLY, engine overheating occurs because the owner fails to maintain his car's cooling system. Maintenance requires draining and flushing the system at least once every two years, seeing that components (hoses, drive belt, radiator-pressure cap and thermostat) are operational, and filling the system with ethylene glycol coolant.

Coolant recovery system installation

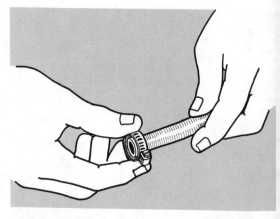

2. HOSE CLAMPS should be used at both ends of the radiator overflow hose. That hose usually runs from the radiator neck down alongside the radiator.

■ IT'S JUST A see-through container that catches overflow from your car radiator. If you have one you take it for granted. If you install it following instructions, you'll wonder how you ever got along without it.

The container is essentially an expansion tank. It is mounted near the radiator and is connected by the radiator overflow hose. It makes a sealed system of your cooling system.

5. THE OVERFLOW bottle, hoses in place, is positioned and held with sheet-metal screws. Holes drilled for the screws shouldn't be too big.

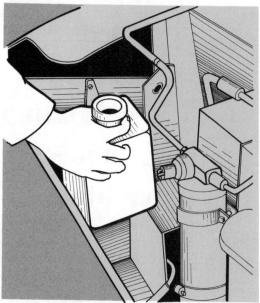

1. OVERFLOW BOTTLE, from a kit such as parts stores offer, should be mounted high in engine compartment near the radiator. A spot ahead of the radiator, perhaps inboard of a front fender, is preferred.

As your engine heats up, expansion takes place in the system and coolant is forced into the tank rather than lost on the road. As your engine cools, temperature and pressure are reduced and coolant is drawn back into the radiator from the tank.

Consider the many advantages:

• You can visually check the coolant level. You don't have to remove the radiator cap and peer inside.

• You eliminate the danger of removing the radiator cap to be confronted by a scalding geyser.

• You save costly antifreeze, now at record high prices.

• A sealed system keeps air out of your cooling system, reducing corrosion and bubbling that impairs heat transfer.

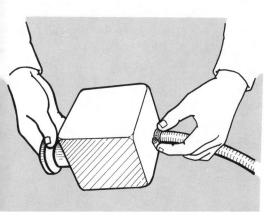

3. THE OVERFLOW HOSE goes over a flange on the bottom of the bottle. Slip a clamp over the hose, install it, then slide the clamp into place.

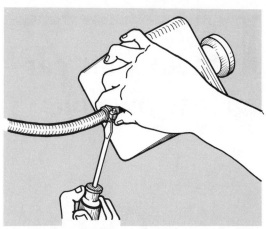

4. TIGHTEN THE CLAMP holding the overflow hose in place at the bottom of the bottle as well as the other clamp at the radiator end of the hose.

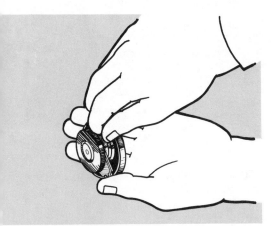

6. NEW RADIATOR CAP comes with overflow bottle kit. The cap's rubber seal is necessary in order to seal the cooling system; make sure it's in place.

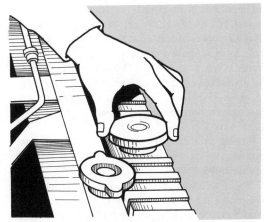

7. INSTALL THE CAP after filling the radiator with a 50/50 mixture of ethylene glycol antifreeze and water. Fill it to the top.

8. FILL THE OVERFLOW bottle halfway with antifreeze. Most bottles have "Min" and "Max" marks; a level midway between them is right.

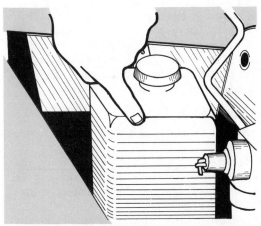

9. LEVEL WILL RISE as the engine warms coolant. That's why the "Max" marking leaves some unfilled capacity—for expansion. Don't overfill.

Protect your car against the cold

■ A RECENT STUDY tells us that the number of engine starting failures reaches a peak in winter.

Across the board, the study shows that where maintenance is practiced, the starting trouble is lowest. In New England, for example, 32 percent of those surveyed winterize their cars and 22 percent have starting failure. Conversely, in seven states taken as a group—Minnesota, North and South Dakota, Missouri, Kansas, Iowa and Nebraska—25 percent of the group surveyed perform prewinter maintenance and 26 percent of them have trouble.

Trying to avert a mechanical problem is just one reason for winterizing a car. Another is to minimize hazards to safety.

To try to touch all the bases in this article—so you don't miss anything when you go to work winterizing your car—we have literally charted a course for you to follow by listing what should be done. Information accompanying each task will allow you to do the work more competently or more easily.

Of course, you may not have to do everything we suggest. It depends on what services you had done in the last couple of months. For instance, if you've just tuned up the engine, you shouldn't have to do it again. However, going into winter with an ignition system which hasn't been serviced since last winter is inviting trouble.

Battery checks

• Replace a battery that is cracked or has eroded terminals.
• Before testing with a battery hydrometer, add water if the electrolyte level is low and give the battery a high-rate charge for 30 minutes or drive the car for a few hours.
• A difference of .050 or more specific gravity points between high and low readings signifies a bad battery. Replace it.

USE CHARGER, if necessary, to bring your battery up to full charge for winter starting.

• Remove the battery and scrub it with diluted ammonia or baking soda solution. Flush with water, being sure the vent caps are tight and covered with tape. Clean the battery carrier, too.
• If the battery shows less than full charge (that is, an overall specific gravity of 1.260), charge it on a slow-rate charger.
• Ideally, a sealed battery should be load-tested to determine its condition. However, in the absence of a 300-amp. load tester and voltmeter, refer to the battery's built-in charge indicator, which provides an indication of battery condition.

Service battery cables

• Replace cables having split or frayed insulation or badly eroded terminals.
• Disconnect cables using a terminal puller, if necessary. Clean terminals with a wire brush.
• Reinstall cables, tightening terminals to posts securely. A chief cause of hard starting is improperly secured terminals. If you have a problem

getting a terminal to bottom on the battery post, place a wrench socket of suitable size over the terminal and *gently,* very gently, tap the terminal down until it won't go any more.

YOUR BATTERY can't deliver if terminals and posts aren't clean.

Clean or replace plugs

• Sparkplugs with worn electrodes, broken insulators or damaged shells should be replaced.
• Sparkplugs with minimum electrode wear can be cleaned, regapped and returned to service.

Replace distributor parts

• Replace any part—cap, rotor or coil—that shows damage or a sign of damage. "A sign of damage" would be a trail of carbon inside a distributor cap, which signifies a crack.

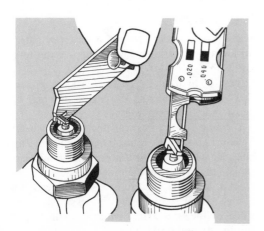

Servicing the distributor

• If you have to replace breaker points, replace the condenser, too.
• If new points aren't needed, pass a fine-cut ignition file through the old points one time to clean them before setting gap.
• An oily smudge on contact points may indicate a clogged PCV system that has caused vapors to be forced into the distributor.
• Make sure that the condenser and primary wire insulation is in one piece. A bare wire can ground out and bring the engine to a dead stop. See that wires are secured firmly to terminals.
• If your car has electronic ignition, it has no points and condenser. Setting dwell is not necessary. Setting ignition timing is.

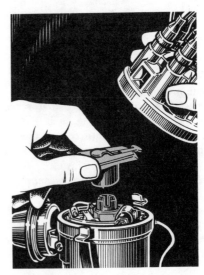

REMOVE distributor cap and rotor and clean and inspect them thoroughly.

Examine secondary cables

• Replace cables if insulation is cracked, split or brittle.
• Make sure the cables are firmly seated in the distributor and coil towers and on sparkplugs. Though lack of contact is involved in most road calls, the problem in most cases is loose wires rather than a defective system.

Service air and fuel filters

• Shine a light inside the air filter. If the filter is very dirty, replace it. If it's not too dirty, dislodge particles by slamming the filter on a hard surface.
• Replace the fuel filter as often as this is stipulated in your owner's manual.

Set automatic choke

• Do this only if the engine becomes hard to start when the weather turns and all other bases have been touched. If the choke is adjustable, turn it one notch at a time to the "rich" side. See if starting gets better.

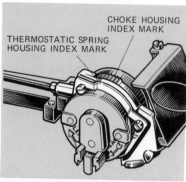

CHOKE ADJUSTMENT is especially important for proper cold starts.

Service cooling system

• Drain and flush, if necessary.
• Inspect hoses and test the radiator pressure cap.
• Add ethylene glycol antifreeze in the proportion necessary to bring protection against freezing in line with the lowest anticipated temperature in your area. *Important:* Use top-quality antifreeze.
• Inspect drive belts. Replace if cracked or frayed. Adjust if necessary to bring them to adequate tension—¼ to ½-inch play when pressed midway between pulleys.

PROPER drive-belt adjustment is necessary for generator and alternator.

Lubricate

• Change oil, if necessary. Drivers in most of the country should select a 10W-30 or 10W-40 motor oil. Where temperatures are consistently between 20° and below 0°F a 5W-30 motor oil may be necessary. If you decide to use a single-viscosity oil and your owner's manual says to use 10W because of the low temperature where you live, avoid sustained high-speed driving.
• Grease the chassis and body points. Shoot some powdered graphite into door locks to try to avert frozen locks.

Get tires in shape

• Mount snow tires (are they in good shape?), storing the tires you've removed in a clean, dry, cool and closed area away from water, petroleum products, electric motors and heat sources. Place tires on their sidewalls on a flat surface—don't stand them on the tread. Place white sidewall tires whitewall-to-whitewall, one on top of the other to protect the white rubber. If tires remain mounted on wheels, reduce inflation to 12 to 16 p.s.i.
• If you buy new snow tires and want metal studs, now's the time to get them. The depth of the stud holes molded into winter tire treads and the lengths of studs are carefully matched. In even a few miles of travel, tire treads wear enough, and fill with enough dirt and grit, to disrupt the stud hole-stud relationship. Only new or newly retreaded tires should be studded, if the law in your state permits studded tires.
• If snow tires were not mounted in storage and are to be put back on wheels, the assemblies should be balanced.
• Maintain recommended air pressure and check it often. Do not reduce inflation pressure to increase traction. Tire makers say that this is a fallacy because underinflated tires get less of a grip on slippery surfaces.

Test brakes

• See that the fluid level in the master cylinder is no less than ¼ inch below the top of the reservoir's lip.
• Test the hydraulic system for leaks by pressing down on the pedal with the engine running. The pedal should be firm and not fade.
• If lining (pad) thickness has not been examined in 12,000 miles, remove one front wheel and one rear wheel and do it now. You should have no less than $\frac{1}{32}$ inch of lining thickness left. *Important:* If you have to replace the linings (pads) of one wheel, replace the linings of the other wheel on the same axle. Failure to do this will result in unequal braking.

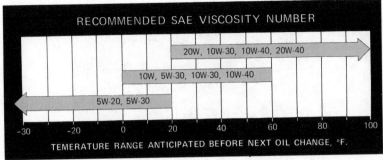

MULTI-VISCOSITY motor oils cover wide ranges of temperature.

Check visual equipment

• Replace windshield wiper blades if the rubber feels flabby rather than firmly resilient or if blades don't sweep water cleanly away.
• Make sure the windshield washers work and that nozzles are aimed to squirt water over the area swept by wipers. Nozzles may be bent to aim them properly. If nozzles are clogged, clear the stoppage with a thin piece of wire.
• Fill the windshield washer reservoir. If your area is subjected to freezing temperatures, the fluid you use should be an antifreeze type. *Caution:* Make certain the label on the container of antifreeze you buy assures you that the product is harmless to paint. If it doesn't, don't use the product.
• Check to see that all lights and warning signals are working. If one isn't, find out why and fix it.
• Are defrosters working properly?
• Test the horn. It may be needed to get you out of a sticky situation one of these winter days.

Other Checks

• The exhaust system should be in good shape. There should not be any evidence of holes or rust. Accidental carbon monoxide poisoning cases are more numerous in winter than at any other time.
• See that the heater works and throws out enough warm air to make you comfortable.
• Get winter emergency equipment out of storage and into your car if it isn't already there. This should include a good ice scraper, shovel, extra emergency flares and tire chains (if you use chains). *Important:* If you place extra weight in

the rear to attain better traction, make sure it's placed over or ahead of the rear axle. Weight behind the rear axle can reduce vehicle stability and front-wheel traction.

Cold-start tips

Once your car is all checked out and ready to go, chances are in your favor that the engine is going to start. But there's always the possibility of a sudden, severe cold snap that could hamper starting. Here are a few extra tips that may help the situation:
• Don't pump the accelerator pedal. Doing so will send raw gas into the cylinders that will tend to flood the engine on a cold day.
• If the engine does flood, turn off the ignition key. Hold the accelerator pedal to the floor (do *not* pump it) and turn on the ignition, cranking the engine in five-second bursts. Don't overdo this since you don't want to add a dead battery to your trouble. If the engine won't start after a reasonable number of five-second bursts, allow it to remain idle for 5 to 10 minutes. Then try it again.
• If the weather is severely cold for a sustained period, a 75 or 100-watt light bulb kept burning under the hood will help keep the temperature of the battery high enough so it will provide a good kick in the morning.
• If you live in really cold country and oil tends to gel overnight so engine cranking is sluggish, you should use a dipstick heater. The heater slides into the dipstick tube and is plugged into house current.
• Whenever you start a car, keep all lights and accessories turned off. The engine stands a better chance of getting going if it doesn't have to share current with other parts.

MANY PEOPLE consider tile to be the most luxurious material for countertops. With the variety of colors, sizes, shapes and textures, tile's design effects range from elegant to rustic. Whichever style you decide on, the only skills you'll need to master are cutting and fitting the plywood base and gluing the tiles down evenly in a preplanned layout.

Countertop installation in tile or laminate

■ The material you choose for resurfacing a kitchen counter has to be special: It must stand up to impact, heat and frequent cleaning with strong detergents. It must resist scratching and staining, and the finish must be stable enough for food preparation. It has to be affordable and good-looking.

Ceramic tile and plastic laminate both meet these requirements. Both are super-hard and come in many designs. And they're easy to install. Each requires only a few special tools.

Working with ceramic tile

Ceramic tile comes in such a wide variety of shapes, sizes, colors and textures that you can create a tile countertop to complement any home decor.

There are three types of tile: glazed, unglazed and quarry tile. In manufacturing glazed tile, the surface of the tile body is first coated with color and then with a glass-like substance that serves to seal the porous clay. Glazed tiles are the softest and easiest to cut.

In unglazed tiles, the color permeates the tile body. The density of the clay makes them extremely stain-resistant. Porcelain tiles are unglazed tiles that are the least likely to stain.

Quarry tiles are more porous and, therefore, more likely to stain. Polyurethane sealers are often used to protect quarry tile, though it may not be desirable to use it on surfaces where food is prepared. For countertop installations, it's usually best to use a latex wall and floor tile adhesive.

Grout is used to seal the joints between tiles. It's available in powdered form. There are cement-based grouts and those made to be mixed with a latex solution. Both types are suitable for countertops, though the latex-based grout resists mildew and deterioration somewhat better. Grout color can either blend or contrast with the tile color to create varied effects. Test the grout first to be sure it won't stain the tile surface, particularly if you're working with unglazed tiles.

Build the counter base first, using ¾-in. *exterior* plywood. Do not substitute particleboard. Make cutouts for sinks and countertop ranges.

1 Basic tools and materials for doing a tile countertop are tile adhesive, grout, notched-edge trowel, rubber-faced grouting trowel and a sponge.

2 For straight cuts, use a tile cutter like the one shown. After the tile is scored, press down firmly on the handle to snap the tile along the mark.

3 To make inside cutouts, use a portable sabre saw with a carbide-grit blade. Support the full tile to avoid possible breakage.

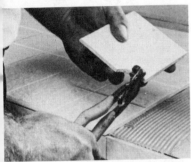

4 Tile nippers are also useful for shaping tiles to fit around cutouts, pipes and fixtures. They're designed to break off small bits without damaging tiles.

5 Use ¾-in. exterior plywood for ceramic tile base. Consider clearance for under-counter appliances when setting base height. Most units require 34½ in.

6 Make a trial layout working from the front edge toward the counter back. Allowing space for grout joints, make a cut mark on tile closest to backsplash.

7 Apply a thin, even coat of adhesive with a smooth trowel edge, then rake it with trowel notches. Glue up small areas until you can set tiles quickly.

8 Press tile firmly into adhesive, starting with the edge trim and working back. Some tiles have self-spacing edge tabs. If yours don't, get plastic spacers.

9 Tiles around sink opening should be cut back a bit from the edge. The space should be small enough to be concealed by Hudee rim or sink's shelf rim.

To prepare for setting tile, skim-coat the base with tile adhesive, using the flat edge of a trowel. Let it dry thoroughly (about four hours). Make a trial layout with the tiles. For tops without cutouts for sinks or ranges, start the layout at the center of the front edge. When the top has a sink cutout, start at the cutout center and work toward either side. Then apply a thin, even coat of adhesive over the skim coat and rake it with the notched trowel edge. Cover only as large an area as you can set with tile in 20 minutes. If skin forms on adhesive, scrape it off and spread a fresh coat. Place tiles immediately.

Let adhesive set for at least 24 hours before grouting. Follow the maker's instructions, mix the grout and apply it to the tiles with a sponge.

Then force it into joints with a rubber-faced trowel. Strike the joints with a popsicle stick or similar tool. As grout begins to set, clean excess from the tile with a clean sponge, rinsing the sponge frequently. Work quickly—grout left on tiles for longer than an hour is almost impossible to remove.

Let grout set for at least 24 hours before exposing it to water. Remove grout haze with a soft, dry cloth. Protect joints from mildew by saturating them with lemon oil furniture polish.

10 Grout joints on backsplash should align with those of countertop. If a course needs to be cut to fit under hanging cabinets, it should be top one.

11 Front edge of backsplash is trimmed with a bullnose-edged piece. With unglazed tiles, you can form bullnose edges yourself with a belt sander.

12 Let adhesive set at least 24 hours before grouting. Use a rubber-faced trowel or squeegee to press grout into joints and remove excess from tile.

13 Use a tongue depressor or similar tool to compact grout and remove buildup at the edges. This technique is called "striking the joints."

14 When the grout begins to set (30-60 minutes), clean any excess from the tile surface with a damp sponge. Rinse sponge often with clean water.

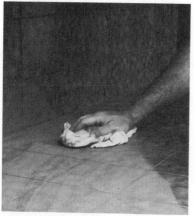

15 Allow grout to dry thoroughly. The grout residue remaining on tiles can be cleaned off with a soft, dry cloth.

16 Finished tile surface can be kept like new with household cleaners.

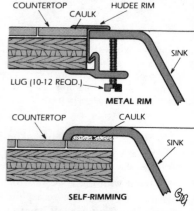

17 Sink with Hudee rim is most popular. Both types are installed in a bead of caulk around the perimeter.

FUNCTIONAL, durable countertop materials can also be elegant-looking; high-pressure plastic laminates prove that point. And you can install them yourself. Laminate is available in a wide range of colors, patterns and finishes. Many people prefer to use a portable router for edge trimming, but even if you don't own one, you can get professional results with the hand tools shown.

Working with plastic laminate

Plastic laminate sheets are available in a wide range of solid colors and decorative patterns and in several surface finishes, including gloss, satin and texture. For ease of cleaning, you should avoid textured or deeply embossed patterns. Dark colors are more likely to show scratches.

There are two grades of plastic laminate: standard and vertical. The standard grade, 1/16 in. thick, is the choice for counter (horizontal) applications because it is more durable. Vertical grade is 1/32 in. thick and is used for cabinet sides, doors, furniture and wall treatments.

Stock sheet sizes are as follows: Widths are available in 24, 30, 36, 48 and 60 in. Lengths run 60, 72, 84, 96, 120 and 144 in. Actually, the laminates come slightly larger than these stated sizes to permit flush trimming to standard-size core materials. The standard depth (width) for kitchen countertops is 24 in. overall.

While plastic laminate is quite hard, it is thin and rather brittle. It does not have the practical strength or high-impact resistance until it is bonded to a solid core material. It can be bonded to solid lumber, plywood or particleboard or over old laminate. Exterior-grade plywood or particleboard is ideal for new work, but whatever the surface to be covered, it must be whole and solid, clean, flat and dry.

Fill all voids in the core material, no matter how small or shallow. This is particularly important if you use a piloted router bit for trimming, because the pilot will follow any irregularity causing matching deviations in the laminate edge.

There are two types of contact cement, the adhesive used for bonding the laminate: flammable and nonflammable. It is safest to use the nonflammable type, though it dries a little more slowly than the lacquer-based flammable adhesive. With either type, work in a well-ventilated area. Lacquer thinner should be used to clean off excess contact cement that builds up on the edges.

Laminate will bond properly only to a true plane surface. A belt or finishing sander will be useful for smoothing and leveling large surfaces. You must exercise great care to avoid tipping the sander downhill as it moves past the ends, or you will create a sloping surface. If old laminate is to be resurfaced, it should be sanded thoroughly to provide "tooth" for a good adhesive bond.

The basic steps in applying laminate are cutting, applying adhesive, bonding and trimming. Relatively few tools are required to do these steps. If need be, you can do the job entirely with hand tools.

There are many options for achieving the same

end result. For example, you can cut the laminate with a saw or tin snips, or by scoring and breaking with a plastics scriber. Bonding pressure can be applied with a hammer and wood block, rolling pin or photo print roller. Trimming can be done with a block plane or file.

Power tools let you do the job more quickly and with less effort. Some of the special laminate tools (like the heat gun and special rollers) are not essentials, but they're relatively inexpensive and might even be rented, and you will find them handy.

1 Lamination can be done with keyhole saw, tin snips, plastics scriber, paintbrush, hammer, wood block, roller, rolling pin, mill file and block plane.

2 Most people prefer to use a router with flush and bevel trimmers, a belt sander and a sabre saw with fine-tooth blade. Roller applies adhesive.

3 Special tools include (clockwise from bottom left): laminate edger, laminate trimmer, AR roller, heat gun, J-roller and squeeze roller.

4 Core preparation is step No. 1. For self-edge treatments, where the same material is used on the edge as on the surface, core edge is usually built up with ¾-in. stock for attractive look. Outside corners are often rounded with a sabre saw because square corners are painful to bump into and easily damaged.

5 The core edge must be perfectly straight and at a 90° angle to the surface. Use a belt sander to smooth the curve and flatten the edge. Be careful not to sand too much, and don't rock the sander side to side. A crooked, bellied edge will weaken the bond and also makes for a poor finished appearance.

6 Always cut laminate at least ¼ in. larger overall than needed. Lay out large pieces first, then edge bands. If you cut with a plastics scriber, keep the laminate face up and tape a metal straightedge on the layout marks. Cut approximately halfway through, then bend toward the back surface to snap.

7 Cut sheets face down when using a sabre saw or portable circular saw. Support sheet close to the cutting line to prevent cracking. A white pencil makes layout marks easy to see, since the sheet back is usually gray or brown.

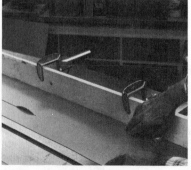

8 When cutting laminate on a table saw, the decorative side should be face up. A fine-tooth carbide blade is best, since chrome-steel blades dull quickly. Clamping a board to the fence keeps laminate from creeping underneath it.

9 When applying laminate to counter surfaces, always apply the edges before applying top. Prop core up about ⅛ in. on work surface and dust well. Apply two coats of contact cement to the core edge and one to laminate back.

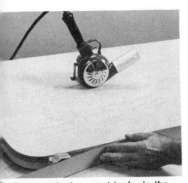

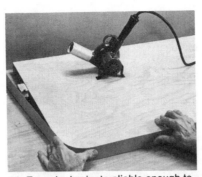

10 Once contact cement is dry to the touch, apply the edge strip. Start at one end and use the work surface as a positioning guide. For better control, you can set an object between the adhesive-coated surfaces to keep them apart.

11 To make laminate pliable enough to bend around a relatively tight radius, you can heat it with a heat gun, heat lamp or hair dryer. If the corner above were a square one, we would have put the end piece on before the front edge.

12 Apply pressure over the entire bonded surface. Tap the surface with a hammer using a wood block to protect the finish, or burnish it with a roller or a wood block. Never apply pressure to laminate extending past the core.

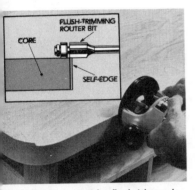

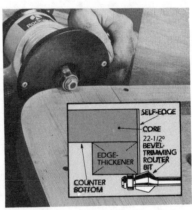

13 Each piece must be flush-trimmed before adding an adjoining piece. A flush-trimmer router bit has a pilot to guide the carbide cutters. It might leave the edge slightly proud. If so, you should level it with a belt sander.

14 If you don't have a router, flush-trim with a scoring tool. Exert downward pressure to guide tool on the adjacent surface. It takes several passes to score laminate halfway through. Then press back on waste to snap off.

15 Edges that don't adjoin a piece of laminate—like the counter bottom—are bevel-trimmed to eliminate sharpness. When bevel-trimming with a router, set depth so bit cuts only laminate's thickness, not into adjacent face.

16 Rollers used to apply contact cement should have a phenolic core and short nap. Line roller tray with aluminum foil to ease cleanup. Make adhesive coats ample, but be careful; drips on edges make trimming and cleanup hard.

17 Contact cement bonds instantly. Use slip sticks to separate glued surfaces until laminate is positioned to cover whole core. Work from one end, removing sticks in succession, allowing the glued surfaces to bond a bit at a time.

18 Apply pressure once the laminate is in place to ensure a good bond. Pay special attention to the edges. A roller like the one shown is perfect for broad surfaces, but a hammer and block of wood or a rolling pin also work.

19 If you're using a router, trim off excess with a flush bit. Then finish the edge with a bevel trimmer.

20 After trimming, go over edges again, either with a J-roller, as shown, or with another burnishing tool.

21 Trimming and beveling bits leave slight ridges. Smooth with medium grit sandpaper or a fine mill file.

22 If you don't have a router with a bevel trimmer, you can use a laminate edger to shave a controlled bevel.

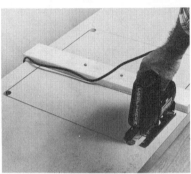

23 Lay out and cut opening for sink. Cut two parallel sides. Attach a cleat to support cutout before making final cuts.

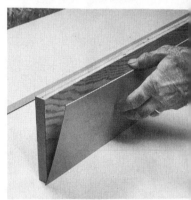

24 Laminate the backsplash in three steps. Apply the end pieces first, the front next, and the top strip last.

25 Align backsplash with back edge of counter and clamp it. Bore pilot holes for No. 8 x 1½-in. wood screws.

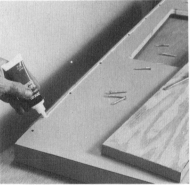

26 A bead of caulking seals backsplash seam. This prevents water seepage that could make the laminate bubble.

27 Install backsplash and countertop on base cabinets as a single unit. Protect corners when moving the piece.

Plastic laminate application

HAND TOOLS YOU WILL NEED

12-15 PT. CROSSCUT SAW

SCORE AWL

SMOOTH FILE

BLOCK PLANE

DIAGONAL CUTTERS

NYLON BRUSH

FRIEZE ROLLER

SCRATCH AWL

SOFT-FACE MALLET

NOTCHED SPREADER

TIN SNIPS

ROLLER

■ IF YOU'VE SHIED AWAY from resurfacing a worn kitchen countertop—or tackling any project that calls for working with plastic laminates—because you felt that applying laminated plastics was beyond your skills, take heart. With average handyman skills, a measure of common sense and the know-how shown on these pages, you'll find that applying laminated plastics can, indeed, be a do-it-yourself project.

In broad terms, working with laminates involves four operations: cutting, spreading the adhesive, bonding, and trimming and finishing. On these pages, we show you how to do all four steps, no matter what tools you may have.

Some basic points to keep in mind:
• Be sure all surfaces are clean. If necessary, dust both core stock and back side of laminate, then wipe surfaces with a rag soaked with lacquer thinner.
• Fill all voids in core surface and edges with quality wood filler. Cut out entirely any large void and glue in a piece of pine.
• Recommended materials for use as core stock are plywood and particle-board. Many pros favor the latter because it's less likely to have voids and thus usually requires less preparation time.
• Applying plastic laminate over a finished surface is not recommended, but occasionally such a bonding will "take." Still, if you want to laminate over a finish, it would be advisable to remove that finish first so that the contact cement will be applied to bare wood.
• Plastic laminate can be applied over old worn plastic laminate if you take precautions. First, test the existing laminate for looseness. It *must be well-adhered*. Then sand its surface thoroughly for good bonding.
• Adhesives. Some contact cements are flammable, and some aren't. If you're using the flammable type, work only in a well-ventilated room and make certain there are no open flames or sparks around. If you're working over a finished floor, protect it with a dropcloth.
• Cutting. Particles of laminate are certain to fly about as the material is cut with power saw or router. *Make it a rule to always wear safety goggles when cutting the material.*

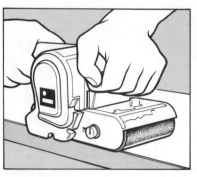

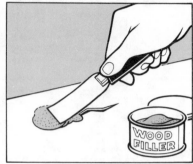

About contact cement

Apply contact cement to the core materi as quickly and evenly as possible. Unli most glues, contact cement must be "dr before bonding the mating parts. Do n use your fingers to test for dryness; u method shown in drawings 4 and 5 belo natural oils from your skin can make t adhesive ineffective.

Always read the manufacturer's instru tions on the can label before startin There are several types of cements ava able and proper use varies slightly fro one maker to the next. The key point is t working time that the adhesive allow Working time is the period of time aft application of adhesive when effecti bonding can be achieved. Some conta cements have a greater working time th others; you should know just how muc time you have to complete the job.

If too much time is allowed to pass b tween cement "ready" time and bondin both the core material and the lamina should be recoated with contact cemer For best results, do not use contact c ment at temperatures lower than 70° F. the air is dry, so much the better; conta cements dry faster when moisture conte in the air is low.

When the job is finished, tightly seal ca and store in a safe place with other fla mable materials. (Away from high heat ar exposure to direct sunlight.)

Preparing core stock

The importance of core stock being clean, smooth and free of voids cannot be over-stressed. The quickest way to get such a surface is to use a belt sander. Lacking this tool, you can use a finishing sander, or sandpaper wrapped around a block of wood and arm power.

In the above illustration, a belt sander is shown being used to make certain that the top edge of the applied laminate self-edge is perfectly flush with the core top surface. If it isn't, an imperfect glue line between the top piece of laminate and the self-edge is almost inevitable. Such separations are called delaminations. If you use the belt sander to smooth this edge, be sure to keep it moving in order to prevent any chance of "dishing" along the edge.

The quickest method of filling voids (above) is by pushing in a quality wood filler. Left unchecked, voids can come back to "haunt" the project builder. Since the router cutter-guide follows the core edge when trimming, it will follow any unfilled void to cause an indent in the trimmed laminate. Large voids under new laminate can cause cracks or chips in the plastic if it's bumped by a heavy object.

Since most commercial fillers shrink as they dry, plan on two passes with putty knife and filler. When filler dries, thoroughly sand the entire surface and dust off.

Applying adhesive

There are three ways to apply contact cement. The paint-roller technique shown in drawing 1 is easiest, quickest and best. But make certain you use the right roller cover: one that applies the adhesive evenly, does not deposit lint on the sticky surface. Drawing 2 illustrates the notched-spreader technique. At one time, contact cement makers gave these away with adhesive purchases; now it is hard to buy one. You can, however, use the edge of a serrated trowel with 1/32 to 1/16-in. notches to do the job. Simply pour a puddle of cement on the surface and spread.

Small areas or strips of self-edge are best coated using a small, clean paintbrush. Though some advocate an animal-hair brush, these do have a tendency to lose bristles. A nylon brush works fine, and a used, stiff one can be rejuvenated for use again with an overnight soaking in contact cement.

To test coated surfaces for readiness, lightly touch adhesive with a piece of brown (kraft) paper. When cement does not stick to paper (5), the surfaces are ready to be bonded.

...tting laminates

...e trickiest part of cutting is making cer-
...in that the piece is well supported while
...e cutting takes place. Damage will occur
...the laminate is allowed to "chatter"
...ile the cutting tool's teeth slice the ma-
...rial. Since the surface (decorative) mate-
...al can be easily chipped off, it should
...ways face the cutting edge of the tool as
...own at right.

For example, when using a fine-tooth
...osscut handsaw, face the decorative
...de up (because the saw cuts on the
...ownstroke and cleans the kerf on the up-
...roke). On a table saw (2), use a carbide-
...pped blade, clamp a strip of laminate to
...e fence to prevent the piece being cut
...om slipping beneath the fence; cut with
...od side up. With a sabre saw, use a fine-
...oth hacksaw blade—and the sabre-saw
...oe insert—while the laminate is well
...upported on each side of the cutting line.
...e easiest method is to use a pair of 2x4s
...cross sawhorses positioned below the
...minate to straddle and parallel the cut-
...ng line. Cut it with face side down. In No.
... use laminate shears to nip off a narrow
...ection before bonding. With a portable
...rcular saw (5), cut the laminate decora-
...ve side down on adequate supports. Use
... carbide-tipped blade set to just clear the
...minate thickness; thus cutting slightly
...to the wood support used below.

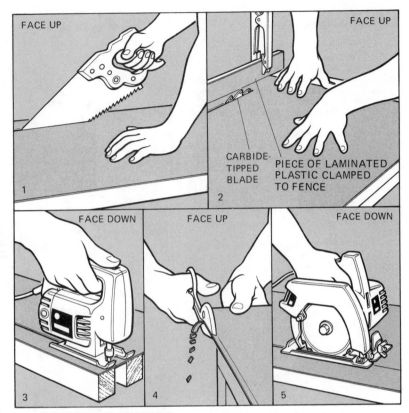

FACE UP

FACE UP

CARBIDE-TIPPED BLADE

PIECE OF LAMINATED PLASTIC CLAMPED TO FENCE

1 2

FACE DOWN FACE UP FACE DOWN

3 4 5

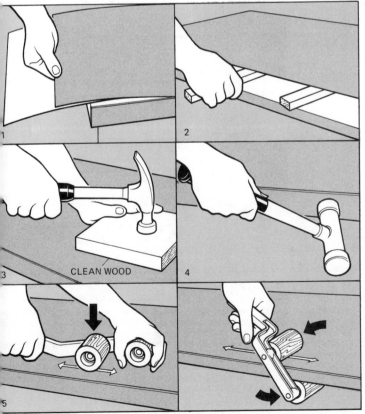

CLEAN WOOD

Bonding laminate

When adhesive has dried, it is necessary to keep
apart the surfaces to be bonded until desired.
Many do-it-yourselfers use a large sheet of brown
(kraft) paper to achieve this (1). This method does
work, but because the paper can be stubborn to
slide out, it often is difficult to keep laminate
correctly aligned over core. A better method is
shown in No. 2. Here, ¾-in. sticks (or dowels) are
spaced about 12 in. apart. Laminate is positioned
over the core and sticks are slipped out one at a
time. All edges of the laminate should be
checked to assure overhang before removing the
first stick. Once the bonding process starts, work
rapidly—sliding out sticks and pressing laminate
into contact with the core material.

When the entire sheet of laminate is in contact
with the core, immediately apply pressure to its
surface. Most laminates need only momentary
pressure. You can apply pressure by any of the
four methods shown in drawings 3 through 6. In
No. 3, it is by sliding a block of hardwood about
and tapping with a hammer. In No. 4, a soft-face
mallet is used to apply pressure to a self-edge
strip. The double roller in Nos. 5 and 6 applies the
best possible pressure—if you use laminates often, you should invest in one. Apply pressure
working outward from the center. If the job is
done properly, it is not necessary to clamp the
workpiece.

Trimming laminate overhang

Since almost all pieces of laminate are cut slightly oversize (larger than the core stock), trimming is usually necessary after bonding. Lacking power tools, you can use a block plane. To avoid gouges, extend the plane iron no more than 1/16th in. Remove excess laminate as close as possible to the core (1); finish trimming with a large, smooth file (2). When filing, remove material on push stroke only.

But power is the easiest way to go. No. 3 shows a router with a carbide straight cutter trimming self-edge. Cutter guide rides the core surface to establish the trimming line. In No. 4, the top piece has been applied and trimmed with a straight cutter; chuck a carbide bevel cutter in router to dress the edge. Laminate trimmer (5) does straight or bevel trimming with one adjustable cutter.

Clean and lubricate bits with pilots after each use to prevent "freezing." Where nonpilot bits are used, apply petroleum jelly to laminate self-edge to prevent cutter scorch marks.

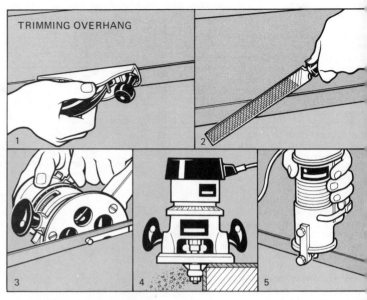

TRIMMING OVERHANG

SCRAP OF PLASTIC LAMINATE

Job cleanup

Never use metal tools to scrape excess adhesive from laminate surface. Instead, use piece of scrap laminate and a rag soaked with lacquer thinner (or contact-cement solvent). Avoid excessive use of solvent. If it penetrates glue line, it will cause delamination. Soften the adhesive with some solvent, scrape with laminate scrap and wipe clean with dry cloth.

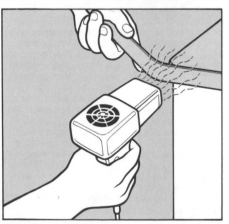

Turning a corner

Conventional plastic laminates have limited flexibility (bend radius). But they can be bent safely around a 7-in. radius at room temperature; tighter if both laminate and core stock are heated. Typical heating instruments are an iron, hair dryer and flameless heater (shown above). Apply two coats of contact cement to the core edge and one coat to the laminate strip. Starting at one end, contact strip to core and work your way toward the bend. When it is reached, heat strip and core and slowly bend strip into contact; hold momentarily. Wear heavy gloves to protect hands from heated surfaces.

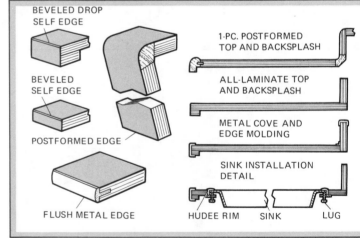

BEVELED DROP SELF EDGE

BEVELED SELF EDGE

POSTFORMED EDGE

FLUSH METAL EDGE

1-PC. POSTFORMED TOP AND BACKSPLASH

ALL-LAMINATE TOP AND BACKSPLASH

METAL COVE AND EDGE MOLDING

SINK INSTALLATION DETAIL

HUDEE RIM   SINK   LUG

Tips about countertops

Typical kitchen countertop treatments are shown above: The postformed type should be done by pros; do-it-yourselfers can safely tackle the standard type with either metal or self-edging. The latter is better looking and generally preferred.

There are two types of self-edge; one has a thickened edge with 3/4-in. square p or plywood fastened to underside of the countertop using glue and annul threaded nails. Since the router cutter rides the strip when trimming the self-ed bottom, set, fill and sand smooth *all* nailheads. A backsplash is set in caulk a permanently attached with 1 3/4-in. wood screws.

Darkroom goofs you can avoid

■ DO YOUR NEGATIVES keep coming out of the tank full of pinholes, streaks, scratches and reticulation even though you faithfully follow all of the customary developing steps? The normal reaction is to blame the film (outdated or damaged) or chemicals (exhausted or contaminated). Actually, it could be that your processing technique has some built-in flaws.

The goal of processing your own film is to produce crisp, brilliant negatives and, ultimately, prints of top professional quality. It doesn't make much sense to shoot the original pictures meticulously and then get careless in the processing stage, especially when it may cost you that "once-in-a-lifetime" shot. The following are 15 of the most common goofs, step by step, that are made in home processing.

1. Touching the emulsion. Because film has a frustrating tendency to curl back into a roll, it is a real challenge to your dexterity to get it onto the reel without touching the emulsion (dull) side. Perspiration and skin oils can leave an indelible fingerprint superimposed on the latent image. If you're not sure you can handle film without touching the emulsion, wear a pair of thin cotton gloves such as those sold for the purpose.

2. Bypassing the predevelopment rinse. When developer is poured into the tank, the film temperature drops suddenly and this "shock" can cause reticulation—a network of thin lines that will be reproduced prominently in the print. You can avoid this by first bathing the film for a few minutes in a filtered water bath at the same temperature as that of the developer. (Water has no chemical effect on the film.)

3. Using impure water. All tap water contains impurities, some of which can cause adverse reactions in photo chemicals. Ideally, distilled water should be used in mixing solutions, but boiled and filtered tap water works equally well.

4. Measuring carelessly. Only beakers made especially for use in photo processing should be used. Inexpensive plastic cooking beakers tend to be less accurate. The beaker should not be held at eye level while water and chemicals are added, but should be placed on a flat surface. Measure water precisely, or your solution will be too strong or too weak.

5. Mixing improperly. It's always a great temptation to dump powdered chemicals into a jar and just shake vigorously until they dissolve. Gentle stirring with a rod is really the only safe mixing procedure. Violent shaking churns the solution into a froth of air bubbles that settle on the film and cause pinholes.

6. Lack of preparation. Before pouring the developer into the tank, all the chemicals you will need should be mixed and filtered and your equipment should be clean and close at hand. Set the timer for the required development time, *less 35 seconds.* Tanks usually require about this long to empty, so by the time you've drained the tank, the development will be stopped at almost the precise time. (The timer should be started when you begin to pour in the developer, not after the tank is full.)

7. Insufficient agitation. Streaky, blotchy film is the result of inadequate agitation. Fresh developer must reach the film at least every 60 seconds during the development or the solution in contact with the film becomes exhausted. As a result, the film may come out underdeveloped. A greater danger is that the developer may become loaded with halide from the film emulsion and spread unevenly in streaks across the film.

8. Violent agitation. This is the other extreme. It doesn't take much action to create air bubbles inside a tank, and air bubbles cause pinholes. Nikor tanks (stainless steel) should be inverted

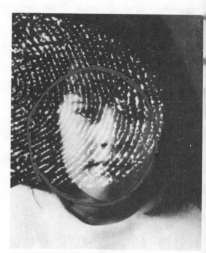

HIGH-TEMPERATURE PROCESSING can soften the emulsion to the point where it loses its grip and begins to slip. Result: ugly blotches like these that ruin the negative. Stick to slower, but safer, standard processing, usually at 68° F.

TELLTALE THUMBPRINT on this blowup is a sign of careless handling during the developing. Skin oils will leave indelible prints on the emulsion.

INFURIATING PINHOLES start out as tiny specks in the negative, but look like baseballs when you blow them up, as above. The cause: Air bubbles in the developer. The cure: Use gentle agitation so as not to whip up a froth.

SPOTS LIKE THESE result from improper mixing. Each was caused by a minute granule of undissolved developer crystal. Even so, filtering the solution before use would have trapped the harmful particles and saved the picture.

SCRATCHES in the emulsion are caused by rough handling in many ways. Careless sponging ruined what would have been a cute candid shot.

INADEQUATE AGITATION during the development can wreck an entire roll of prize shots. Here streaks are from a halide-loaded developer.

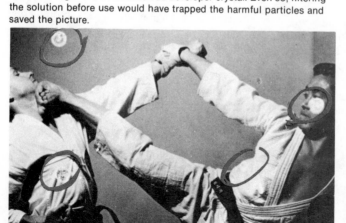

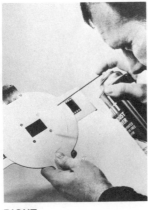

RONG   **RIGHT**

BLOWING IS FINE for starting a charcoal fire, but is no way to remove dust from negatives. Moisture blown onto the surface from your breath will dry as water spots and show up on print. Instead, use a pushbutton can of air. One blast from its jet will safely and effectively whisk away every dust particle.

RONG   **RIGHT**

HOLDING THE FILM in your fingers while you are loading it into a carrier, as at far left, is a sure way to get oily prints all over the emulsion; they will show up later on the print. Grip the film at the edges between fingers and bow it slightly so that it won't touch the carrier as you slide it into position.

gently for agitation and slammed occasionally against a flat surface to burst any air bubbles that may have formed. Don't try this with a plastic tank, however. Twirl the rod in a plastic tank three or four times each way for about five seconds during agitation (every 30 seconds with some developers, every 60 seconds with others).

9. Overdevelopment/underdevelopment. There is a solution for both of these problems, but each is tricky and must be performed with care. Over-developed negatives can be treated with one of several reducers that absorb silver content in equal amounts from the high, middle and low densities, thereby reducing the visual contrast of the negative.

Underdeveloped negatives are more difficult to improve, especially when they are also under-exposed. You simply can't add image detail where none was registered during exposure. The use of an intensifier (silver, chromium, mercury) can add some contrast and occasionally permit you to salvage a negative, but intensifiers have a tendency to stain.

10. Failure to use an acid rinse. Some photographers argue against using an acid stop-bath rinse between development and hypo, claiming that acid causes pinholes. They prefer a water rinse instead. However, those favoring the acid rinse contend that proper agitation during the rinsing phase would prevent gas bubbles from forming and thus eliminate the chance of pinholes.

The purpose of an acid rinse is to stop development immediately by neutralizing any developer that has adhered to the film after the tank is drained. Since water has no chemical effect on film, development can continue during a water rinse, producing overdeveloped negatives. Furthermore, an acid bath helps to remove developer scum and prevents the formation of dichroic fog (red and green stains).

11. Improper fixing. Manufacturers' instructions for using hypo usually say: "Fix two to five minutes." Fixing time will vary from roll to roll. Rather than assume the film is adequately fixed, play it safe by pouring the hypo into a "holding" beaker while you check the film under a strong light. If you spot a milky cast, this is a tipoff that further fixing is required. The image quality of insufficiently fixed film (and prints) will deteriorate rapidly.

There is danger, too, in overfixing both film and prints. Extended "souping" can bleach out most of the image. (Two to three minutes over the recommended time won't hurt.)

12. Using exhausted hypo. Exhausted hypo is loaded with silver thiosulfate compounds that never can be completely removed from films and prints, even with prolonged washing. The results are prominent stains that usually appear long after the films and prints have been processed and dried. Hypo that is being reused should first be tested for potency with Kodak's Residual Silver Test Solution.

13. Careless washing. Films and prints require

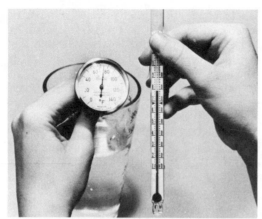

A DARKROOM THERMOMETER should be checked periodically against another thermometer to make sure that it remains absolutely accurate.

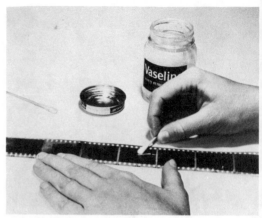

SCRATCHED NEGATIVES often can be salvaged by applying petroleum jelly or a lacquer filler to the damaged areas.

TO KEEP EVERYTHING at the same temperature, put tank and beakers in a tray of water that first has been brought to the correct temperature.

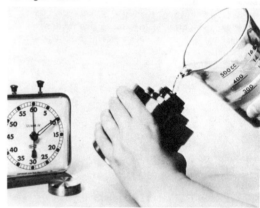

START YOUR TIMER just before you begin filling the developing tank, not after it is full. Tip the tank slightly to prevent air bubbles from forming.

a thorough washing (always in cold water) with *frequent agitation* to remove residual hypo. The flow into the washing tray should be adjusted so there are 12 complete changes of water every hour. Since this is difficult to gauge, try this test: Turn on the water to the flow you intend to use, then pour in a few drops of dye or food coloring concentrate. All traces of the dye should disappear in five minutes. If the dye is still visible after five minutes, increase the flow of water and repeat until the container clears within the set time.

14. Forced drying. Films should never be force-dried by fan, blower heater, hair dryer, or other devices that tend to stir up dust and deposit it on the wet surface of the film. Dust and other foreign matter sticks tenaciously to the film during drying and may even become firmly embedded in the emulsion. Only a second washing or

soaking can safely remove such particles, and even this sometimes fails. If you don't have a film-drying cabinet, the bathroom is the next best place to dry film. Run the shower to settle the dust, then hang the film inside the stall.

Film should not be hung for drying directly from the wash. First, treat it with a wetting solution.

15. Scratching the emulsion. Occasionally, film picks up particles of foreign matter or scum that resist the wetting agent treatment. Only in this case should a sponge sandwich or chamois be used. Wet emulsion is soft and highly susceptible to damage. A bit of grit or film trapped under the sponge or chamois can gouge an irreparable scratch the length of the film. The less you have to touch the film (wet or dry), the better the results you'll get when you go to the enlarger.

GOOD PRINT has a wide tonal range, from white to black and all gray tones between.

Cure muddy photo prints

■ PRINTS FROM photographers, even professionals, are often muddy, murky, dull and lifeless. There are mere grays where there should be blacks, and the whites appear to be seen in dim light through a dirty window. Yet the causes and cures of muddiness are easy to understand.

The first step, of course, is to look closely at your prints. The reason so many people try to sell or show off muddy work is because they're so carried away by the image of the picture itself that they can't take an objective look at how horribly that image is displayed. So take that look: A good print virtually always has at least one spot

of pure, rich black, and one of pure, sparkling white to set off its range of middle tones. If you've deliberately broken this rule, fine—presumably you had a reason. But if your prints accidentally lack true whites or blacks, find out what you're doing wrong.

First, look at your negatives. If they don't cover the full range of tones, from a few, almost black spots of highlight to a few spots of shadow that are almost clear with a wide range of gray tones in between, you'll have trouble getting a good print.

When you take the picture, make sure you expose correctly, then follow the manufacturer's developing times and temperatures *exactly*. Adjust the exposure index setting of your light meter, setting the meter to a slightly higher than normal film speed if your films are

Muddy prints are caused by: (1) overexposure, under-development; (2) too-low paper contrast; (3) thin negative overexposed in printing for deeper blacks; (4) thin negative underexposed for cleaner whites; (5) thin negative ''saved'' as far as possible by contrasty No. 4 paper—but still a bit flat and muddy because of deficiencies in the negative.

consistently overexposed or setting it a bit lower if you normally underexpose negatives.

But most muddy prints are made from negatives that could yield better prints with better work. One of the easiest temptations to bad workmanship is to overexpose and underdevelop the print. In our impatience to see the picture, it's easy to blast a print with so much light that an image will pop into view as soon as the developer hits the paper, or to pull a print out of the developer when it begins to "look all right" under the safelight, even if the entire recommended developing time (usually about a minute) hasn't yet gone by. Unfortunately, that doesn't give the developer time to work evenly and thoroughly on the whole print. As a result, the prints are muddy and often mottled with poor highlight detail.

A second temptation—letting underexposed prints linger in the developer in hopes that they'll somehow improve—will only give you fog, stain, a lack of highlight detail, or all three at once. Never try to make up in development for a gross exposure error. If you have to change development times more than 20 or 30 seconds from the recommended time, remake the print with another exposure (stabilization printing, which gives you no leeway to fool around with processing time, is a great teacher of exposure discipline).

Use the correct exposure

And make sure you have *exactly* the right exposure—often an exposure difference of only 10 or 20 percent can turn a merely adequate print into a good one, or vice versa. Your goal is a print that not only contains a full range of tones, but has all the shadow and highlight details that were in the negative. Correct paper contrast will help with this.

Overdevelopment or underdevelopment can still occur when you follow the paper manufacturer's developing-time recommendations, if your developer is at the wrong temperature or concentration. Underdevelopment (and, frequently, stains) will also occur if you try to process too many prints in a tray of developer or let it get contaminated by stop bath or fixer (refill it with fresh developer when its level drops visibly; discard the whole tray at the first sign of discoloration or sludge).

Proper agitation and inspection make a difference, too. Swishing the paper around in the developer with print tongs (preferably rubbertipped, to prevent print scratching) or by rocking

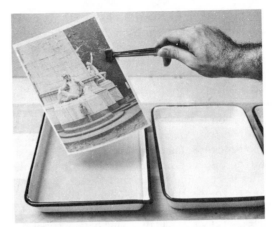

IMPROPER INSPECTION—raising the print from the tray—lets developer run off or oxidize, causing blotchy, uneven development, contrast loss and stains. The proper technique is to hold the print just below the developer surface.

PROPER AGITATION promotes even development. Agitate the print by moving it with tongs (top), taking care not to scratch the print surface, or by rocking the tray (above)—easier with smaller trays, many of which are designed to rock easily, even on flat surfaces.

the tray will ensure that development starts and continues evenly; agitation in the stop bath means that it will stop evenly, too. And agitation in the fixing bath for just the right amount of time will ensure prints that (if properly washed) will last for years. Agitation is the right way to handle a print—but hauling it out of the developer for inspection is the wrong way; developer drains off in spots, oxidizes in others, and that's another cause of uneven development. The best way to inspect a print is in a good white light, after it's been developed and fixed, but learn, too, to compensate for the slight differences in tonality between a processed, wet print and a dry one—what you see in the fixing bath is not quite what you'll get.

If you don't work in your darkroom very often, your chemicals and paper may hang around for months before they're finally used up, and can go stale in the meantime. To prevent this, buy small quantities of paper (even though it costs less per sheet in larger packages), and refrigerate it between darkroom sessions (let it get back to room temperature before you use it).

Mix just what you'll use

Your chemicals, especially developers, should be mixed up only in batches just big enough to fill the biggest tank or tray you use. Keep records of how much you use each chemical, discarding it when it's been used to its rated capacity; the lives of many film developers can be extended, though, by adding a "replenisher" after each use. Stale paper can sometimes be salvaged by adding Kodak Anti-Fog to your developer, but fresh paper will do an even better job.

Stale materials may cause stains, veiled highlights that never show pure whites, or fog that covers the whole paper, including borders. It usually prevents both proper blacks and whites from forming; in fact, the inability to get a proper black, no matter how much you expose the paper, is usually a sign of staleness.

But the inability to get a proper white is more often an effect of light fog. Fog that covers the whole paper visibly is usually caused by light leaks. Darkrooms that look dark when you first turn off the light may not be. A few small light leaks can sometimes be tolerated for printing (but never for film loading) provided none of them admits enough light to illuminate the darkroom (if you can see where you're going in the "dark," it's too light) and none shines directly on the paper. Check for enlarger light leaks, too.

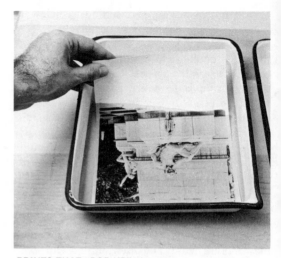

PRINTS THAT "POP UP" almost as you put them into the developer are overexposed; shortening developing time this way seems like a great time-saver, but the developing is uneven and blotchy with poor contrast.

Fog that just veils the highlights is harder to spot. Usually it comes from safelights. The easiest test is to unpack and expose a sheet of paper in complete darkness, then partially cover it with a box and turn the safelights on again. After five minutes, move the box to uncover half of the remaining area; then develop. If you can see a shadow line across the print, you have a fogging problem. Such fog can also come from light that bounces from a white easel back up to the paper emulsion.

Muddy prints are low in contrast, but not all poor contrast is due to the mud-producing errors noted above. Low-contrast subjects (often the result of shooting on a cloudy day) can explain a few "flat" prints; under or overexposed negatives that lack full tonal range will explain even more. These errors can be partially corrected (see Fig. 4) by printing on a "harder," or higher-contrast paper, such as Nos. 4, 5 or Agfa Brovira 6, just as soft papers (No. 1) can help with negatives too high in contrast. If you don't want to stock several paper grades for fear the less-used grades will go stale, use a variable contrast paper (though you'll still need graded papers for contrasts above No. 4 or so). Dust or dirt on your enlarging lens will also cut contrast, as will a cheap, low-grade lens (the difference between enlarger lenses is less in detail resolution than in contrast). Condenser enlargers will also give a bit more contrast than diffusion-type ones.

FILM LOADERS and accessories.

Load your own 35-mm film cartridges

WHAT'S THE BEST photo equipment investment you can make? If you use a 35-mm camera, the answer is a bulk loader. Fill it up, use its contents once, and it has paid for itself. It will keep on cutting your film costs a third or more. And you'll be able to use some special-purpose films you just can't buy by the roll.

Exact costs vary. Discounts are available on both factory loads and bulk rolls. The number of uses you can get from a cartridge depends on how carefully you (or the lab you send your film to) open them, and how free you keep them from dust. You can even reuse factory-loaded cartridges—except for Kodak's, which must be pried, not popped open, and can't be reused.

You can bulk-load quite a number of the films you now buy in cartridges—plus several that don't come in factory loads. There are black-and-white films from Kodak, Ilford, Luminos and Supreme, plus the super-sharp, almost-grainless H&W Control films. In color, you can get Kodak Ektachromes and Vericolor II (but not Kodachrome or Kodacolor).

Most well-stocked photo stores carry at least some bulk films.

Bulk rolls come in lengths of 100, 50 or 27½

feet. The large economy-size 100-footers are really the most economical, but you may prefer shorter rolls of film you use less often.

Today's loaders are light-tight and require darkness only for the few moments it takes for you to put the bulk roll in. If you lack a darkroom, you can use a light-tight changing bag; in a pinch, you can even do it at night under the covers of your bed or in a closet.

Actually, there are two light-tight compartments in these loaders: The large one holds the bulk roll, and the smaller, with its own door, holds the cartridge. Connecting them is a light-tight slit, the light trap, designed to let the film be drawn out of the big compartment.

To load a cartridge, you first open it and remove its spool, then attach the spool to the film end protruding through the light trap. With the film coming from your right, the spool's long end should point toward you.

Reassemble the cartridge around the spool, insert it under the crank in the loader, close the light-tight door, and wind till you have enough film in the cartridge. Then open the door, remove the cartridge, and cut and trim the film end. Some cameras will require that you trim for this. Most cameras will do nicely with a short, diagonal cut as shown below.

your leader like those on factory loads or 27½-foot rolls, and you can get trimming templates

There are two basic types of loaders: Inexpensive, under-$10 ones, use felt-lined slots as light traps. The felt works, but the longer you own the loader, and the more you use it, the greater the chance that a sharp bit of dust will embed itself in the felt and scratch your film.

More expensive models (still under $20) have light traps that can't scratch the film because they never touch it. Instead, a door clamps tight against the film when you open the cartridge compartment, but opens wide to pass the film through freely when the cartridge-compartment door is closed. Interlocks prevent opening the cartridge compartment till you've closed the light trap; but you must remember to open the trap when you wind the film to prevent scratches.

These models also have counters that click off the number of exposures you've wound; felt-trap models usually just have charts telling how many crank winds correspond to what number of exposures.

Most models of the same type work about equally well, though the tiny, light unbranded model would chew film if you set its lid at the wrong angle, and the Premier had the best interlock, but the worst crank.

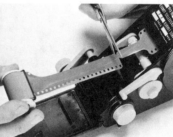

SHORT 27½-foot rolls have a pre-cut tongue to fit slotted cartridge spools (left), a film leader and a new tongue every 36 exposures. Longer rolls save you more

LONGER, 100-foot and 50-foot rolls must be taped to the film spool (left) and cut at the end of each roll (center). The leader must also be cut in the end (right)

Darkroom tips for photographers

ENVELOPE KEEPS TEST STRIPS HANDY: Photographic test strips left lying loose in your enlarging paper box can be hard to find in the dark. Keep them in a manilla envelope, cut open as shown above, and glued to the inside of the enlarging paper box lid.

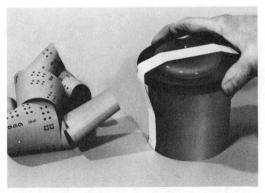

TAPE OVER FILM PREVENTS MISTAKES: If you don't develop your film right after you load it into your film tank you may forget you've loaded it—or forget what type of film you've loaded. Fastening a piece of tape around the lid will remind you (and others) that the tank is loaded. Write the film type and developing time on the tape.

DARKROOM SHELF FITS ON LAUNDRY TUB: If you're using a laundry tub, either single or double, for a darkroom sink, here's a shelf that will stretch your effective counter area—and will drain off easily into the tub.

Attach three 5-inch shelf brackets to a suitable piece of scrap lumber, as shown, so the brackets will fit snugly over the side or divider of the tub. A coat of epoxy paint will make it waterproof and stain-resistant. It's handy for holding trays or developing tanks, and for mixing chemicals.

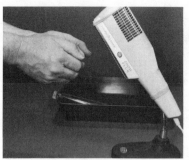

CLEAN, DRY HANDS are necessary to make sure enlarging paper doesn't become contaminated in the darkroom. A hair dryer fastened to a gooseneck or other stand allows you to hold your hands in the airstream for drying.

A CLOTHESPIN will keep a thermometer from falling into a tall bottle when you take temperature readings.

TINY SCRATCHES on a negative are big lines on an enlargement. A tiny amount of petroleum jelly applied to the negative with your finger will fill the scratch and keep it from showing on the enlargement.

A SMALL CAMERA may be supported on many surfaces with a spring photo clamp. The swivel-bolt device is fitted with a bolt, which is then screwed into the tripod socket.

THIS CHART makes it easy to plot the depletion of photo chemicals. Using manufacturer's specs, compute the number of prints of each size obtainable from each batch of chemicals. Draw chart showing each print capacity and mark off the number of prints of each size as they are sent through each bath. When chart indicates solution is exhausted, replace with fresh batch.

WHEN USING your camera's self-timer or when making long exposures, light may enter the camera through the eyepiece if you're not looking through the viewfinder. To eliminate the problem, cover the eyepiece with black tape after composing and focusing.

WHEN PACKING or repacking photo gear, it's easy to leave behind a minor accessory or even a lens if you're in a hurry. An inventory card kept in your bag lets you check off each item as it goes in.

A ¼-20 NYLON NUT glued to the base of a 110 camera makes it suitable for use with a tripod. Cyanoacrylate glue works well.

TAPE a ¼-inch rod, slightly off center, to the underside of a developing tray. When prints are in the solution, set the tray rocking. The liquid will surge to and fro several times before stopping. By repeating this agitation every 10 seconds or so, prints will be more evenly developed.

INDEX · VOLUME 6

_____ A _____

BC computer, 679
coustic coupler modem, 705
nalog information: computers, 704
ntifreeze: in auto cooling system, 736
SCII format: computer languages, 707
SSEMBLY (computer language), 688
tos
 coolant recovery system, 738
 cooling system maintenance, 733
 engine overheating, 737
 protecting in winter, 740

_____ B _____

andwidth: communication circuits, 704
ar clamps
 making your own, 662
 using, 659
ASIC (computer language), 688
attery: auto battery checks, 741
ench: circular saw, 654
nary number system, 682, 703
ts, 682, 705
ades
 circular saw, 644, 648
 circular saw deburring jig, 652
 circular saws, 650
lletin boards: communicating with computers, 702
tes, 682, 705

_____ C _____

clamps, 658
bles: making for your computer, 708
arbide blades: circular saw, 650
ssette tapes
 care of computer tape drives, 713
 computer peripheral, 680
athode ray tubes, 690, 696
ntral processing unit (CPU), 683
ramic tile, 744
rcular saws
 bench, 654
 blades, 644, 648, 650
 deburring jig, 652
 how to use, 644
 safety, 644
 sharpening, 650
amps
 auto radiator hose, 733
 bar, 662
 choosing, 658
 how to use, 659, 662, 663
 machine-vise, 663
ock movements, 665, 669, 671

Clocks
 Connecticut shelf, 665
 Heirloom wall clock, 669
 Wall clock from your lathe, 671
Closets
 bedroom, 676
 built-in, 673
 free-standing, 677
 linen, 677
Coaxial cable, 703
COBAL (computer language), 688
Computers
 binary number system, 682
 cables: making your own, 708
 care, 711
 central processing unit (CPU), 683
 cleaning screens, 713
 communicating with, 702
 data processing, 680, 689
 disc drives, 713
 education: use in, 701
 ergonomics, 716
 hardware, 680
 history, 679
 introduction to, 679
 keyboards, 711
 languages, 688
 logic gates, 682
 memory, 683
 microcomputers, 681
 modems, 704
 monitors, 690, 696
 printers, 685, 714
 security, 707
 software, 680, 689
 spreadsheets, 689
 surge protectors, 712
 word processing, 689
 workstation, 711, 716
Concrete
 blocks, 727
 driveways, 724
 expansion joints, 726
 footings, 723, 728
 forms, 727
 mixing, 723, 725, 727
 patio slabs, 721
 pouring slabs, 723, 725
 premixed, 727
Concrete blocks
 guide to, 732
 how to lay, 727
Coolant: in auto cooling systems, 733
Cooling systems
 auto, 733
 coolant recovery system, 738
 overheating, 737
 winter protection, 740
Countertops
 installing, 744
 laminate, 744, 751
 tile, 744

_____ D _____

Dado: cutting with circular saw, 646

Daisy wheel printers, 686
Darkroom
 common goofs, 755
 mixing chemicals, 762
 techniques, 755
Darkroom tips, 765, 766
Data processing, 680, 689
Decimal number system, 682
Digital information: computers, 703
Disc drives
 care, 713
 computer peripheral, 680
Display devices
 cleaning, 713
 computer, 690, 696
Distributor: checking auto, 741
Doors: closet, 674, 675
Dot matrix printers, 685
Drivebelts: checking auto cooling system, 734
Driveways: pouring concrete, 724
Drywall: installing, 674

_____ E _____

ENIAC computer, 680
Ergonomics, 716

_____ F _____

Fibre-optic cable, 703
Film: loading your own cartridges, 763
Finishes
 computer workstation, 716
 concrete slabs, 726
 Connecticut shelf clock, 665
 Heirloom wall clock, 669
Flat screens
 computer, 696
 TV sets, 696
Floppy discs
 care, 712
 computer peripheral, 684
Footings
 for concrete block walls, 728
 how to pour, 723, 728
Forms: concrete, 721, 725, 726
FORTRAN (computer language), 688
Framing walls, 674
Fuel filters: checking auto, 741

_____ G _____

Gas plasma computer display screens, 698
Grout: with ceramic tile, 744

_____ H _____

Handscrew clamps, 659
Hexadecimal number system, 688
Hold-down clamps, 661

_____ I _____

IBM computer: making your own cables, 708

L

Lathe projects: wall clock, 671
LCD displays, 691, 697
Linen closets, 678
Liquid crystal computer display
    screens, 694
Logic gates, 682

M

Machine-vise clamp: making your
    own, 663
Memory
    external, 684
    random-access-memory (RAM),
        684
    read-only-memory (ROM), 683
Microcomputers
    defined, 681
    packaged systems, 687
Microwave communication, 703
Miter clamps, 660
Miter joints: cutting, 666
Modems (computer peripheral),
    704
Monitors: computer, 690
Mortar: laying concrete blocks,
    727

P

PASCAL (computer language),
    688
Patios: concrete, 721
Photography
    avoiding printing problems, 759

darkroom problems, 755
darkroom tips, 765, 766
loading film cartridges, 763
Pictures
    avoiding developing problems,
        755
    proper exposure, 761
Pipe clamps, 660
Pixels: in computer displays, 691,
    697
Plastic laminate
    adhesives, 752
    applying, 744, 752
    countertops, 744
    cutting, 748, 753
    preparing core, 752
Power surges: protecting com-
    puters from, 712
Printers
    care, 714
    daisy wheel, 686
    desk space, 716
    dot matrix, 685

R

Rabbets: cutting, 666
Radiator: auto cooling system, 733
RGB computer displays, 692

S

Satellite communication, 703
Sharpening circular saw blades,
    650
Shelves
    brackets, 674

closet, 676
darkroom, 766
Sparkplugs: checking auto, 740
Spreadsheets, 689
Spring clamps, 660
Static electricity: protecting com-
    puters from, 711
Storage cabinet: computer desk,
    719

T

Table: circular saw, 654
Thermostat: in auto cooling sys-
    tem, 735
Tile
    adhesive, 744
    ceramic, 744
    countertops, 744
Tires: checking, 742
Toggle clamps, 661
TV picture tubes, 690

U

UNIVAC computer, 680

V

Vacuum fluorescent computer dis-
    play screens, 697
Vise: clamp, 663

W

Walls: concrete block, 727
Windshields: checking, 742
Word processing, 689

SHOP GUIDE

CUSTOMARY TO METRIC (CONVERSION) Conversion factors can be carried so far they become impractical. In cases below where an entry is exact it is followed by an asterisk (*). Where considerable rounding off has taken place, the entry is followed by a + or a − sign.

Linear Measure

inches	millimeters
1/16	1.5875*
1/8	3.2
3/16	4.8
1/4	6.35*
5/16	7.9
3/8	9.5
7/16	11.1
1/2	12.7*
9/16	14.3
5/8	15.9
11/16	17.5
3/4	19.05*
13/16	20.6
7/8	22.2
15/16	23.8
1	25.4*

inches	centimeters
1	2.54*
2	5.1
3	7.6
4	10.2
5	12.7*
6	15.2
7	17.8
8	20.3
9	22.9
10	25.4*
11	27.9
12	30.5

feet	centimeters	meters
1	30.48*	.3048*
2	61	.61
3	91	.91
4	122	1.22
5	152	1.52
6	183	1.83
7	213	2.13
8	244	2.44
9	274	2.74
10	305	3.05
50	1524*	15.24*
100	3048*	30.48*

1 yard = .9144* meters
1 rod = 5.0292* meters
1 mile = 1.6 kilometers
1 nautical mile = 1.852* kilometers

Weights

ounces	grams
1	28.3
2	56.7
3	85
4	113
5	142
6	170
7	198
8	227
9	255
10	283
11	312
12	340
13	369
14	397
15	425
16	454

Formula (exact):
ounces × 28.349 523 125* = grams

pounds	kilograms
1	.45
2	.9
3	1.4
4	1.8
5	2.3
6	2.7
7	3.2
8	3.6
9	4.1
10	4.5

1 short ton (2000 lbs) = 907 kilograms (kg)
Formula (exact):
pounds × .453 592 37* = kilograms

Miscellaneous

1 British thermal unit (Btu) (mean) = 1 055.9 joules
1 horsepower = 745.7 watts
= .75 kilowatts
caliber (diameter of a firearm's bore in hundredths of an inch) = .254 millimeters (mm)

Fluid Measure

(Milliliters [ml] and cubic centimeters [cc] are equivalent, but it is customary to use milliliters for liquids.)

1 cu in = 16.39 ml
1 fl oz = 29.6 ml
1 cup = 237 ml
1 pint = 473 ml
1 quart = 946 ml
= .946 liters
1 gallon = 3785 ml
= 3.785 liters
Formula (exact):
fluid ounces × 29.573 529 562 5* = milliliters

Volume

1 cu in = 16.39 cubic centimeters (cc)
1 cu ft = 28 316.7 cc
1 bushel = 35 239.1 cc
1 peck = 8 809.8 cc

Area

1 sq in = 6.45 sq cm
1 sq ft = 929 sq cm
= .093 sq meters
1 sq yd = .84 sq meters
1 acre = 4 046.9 sq meters
= .404 7 hectares
1 sq mile = 2 589 988 sq meters
= 259 hectares
= 2.589 9 sq kilometers

1 atmosphere pressure = 101 325 pascals (newtons per sq meter)
1 pound per square inch (psi) = 6 895 pascals
1 pound per square foot = 47.9 pascals
1 knot = 1.85 kilometers per hour
1 mile per hour = 1.6093 kilometers per hour